PORTON DOWN

75 Years of Chemical and Biological Research

PORTON DOWN

75 Years of Chemical and Biological Research

by

G B CARTER ISO

London: HMSO

© Crown copyright 1992
Applications for reproduction should be made to HMSO
First published 1992

ISBN 0 11 772732 6

HMSO publications are available from:

HMSO Publications Centre
(Mail, fax and telephone orders only)
PO Box 276, London, SW8 5DT
Telephone orders 071-873 9090
General enquiries 071-873 0011
(queuing system in operation for both numbers)
Fax orders 071-873 8200

HMSO Bookshops
49 High Holborn, London, WC1V 6HB
071-873 0011   Fax 071-873 8200 (counter service only)
258 Broad Street, Birmingham, B1 2HE
021-643 3740   Fax 021-643 6510
Southey House, 33 Wine Street, Bristol, BS1 2BQ
0272 264306   Fax 0272 294515
9–21 Princess Street, Manchester, M60 8AS
061-834 7201   Fax 061-833 0634
16 Arthur Street, Belfast, BT1 4GD
0232 238451   Fax 0232 235401
71 Lothian Road, Edinburgh, EH3 9AZ
031-228 4181   Fax 031-229 2734

HMSO's Accredited Agents
(see Yellow Pages)

and through good booksellers

*Cover photograph by Colonel R D George L/RAMC DNBCC
Winterbourne Gunner*

Contents

Foreword

by Field Marshal Sir Richard Vincent GBE KCB DSO

As Chief of the Defence Staff, I am pleased to put on record the admiration and thanks of all those generations of Servicemen and women whose great trust and confidence in the work of Porton Down over three-quarters of a century is the true measure of the Establishment's achievement. It is an accident of history – but a very timely one so far as your 75th Anniversary is concerned – that some of your very finest work in support of the Armed Forces, and more recently the United Nations Special Commission on Iraq, has been achieved in your 75th year.

The threat that chemical or biological weapons may be used creates immense challenges for modern civilised governments and this is especially so within the sensitivities of an international coalition such as that on which the whole United Nations effort depended in 1991 during Operation DESERT STORM. I know from my very direct and personal involvement in these matters at the time that it was the sheer quality and extraordinary responsiveness of the staff at Porton Down that gave the Government the confidence to make the very tough and timely decisions needed to protect our forces.

In the wider field of CB arms control, Porton Down has also played a leading part – not just in a national sense – but in so thoroughly informing our delegation in Geneva that they were able to bring a quite exceptional influence to bear on various aspects of these complex negotiations. Only time will prove the success, or otherwise, of our international CB arms control efforts, but with Porton's support we have made some valuable progress compared with the weak and seriously flawed conventions of the past. Despite these serious efforts to achieve more effective CB arms control measures, our past experience tells us that none of this will change human nature. Some nations and their leaders will continue to cheat and conceal illegal activities whatever international treaties and conventions their governments may have signed and ratified. We cannot, therefore, responsibly just rest on these treaties as the sole basis of our future security in these difficult and complex areas that so threaten our security if we are deceived and outwitted. We have to underpin them with deep, defensively directed research into protective measures against chemical and biological weapons so that we can constantly monitor their effectiveness and keep up our guard.

It is as a direct result of the efforts at Porton Down that in the Middle East in early 1991 the British Armed Forces, and their civilian colleagues with them, were among the best equipped and protected of any in the Gulf. You had only to visit the operational theatre at the time, as I did, to realise how highly our allies valued our equipment and advice in this area which, in a diplomatic sense, were worth their weight in gold.

These testing events over the past 18 months indicate the value of Porton Down's capabilities built up over many years. On its 75th Anniversary I am therefore pleased to congratulate CBDE on it achievements over the past 75 years which came to such a remarkable climax in the Middle East last year. For the future, I am confident that our armed forces can count on the same measure of professional and dedicated support in this important aspect of our defence capability as we have been fortunate to receive in the past.

The Headquarters Building at CBDE Porton Down. The facade is almost as it was in 1918, though in earlier times it was much obscured by surrounding huts.

RICHARD VINCENT
Chief of the Defence Staff

21 February 1992

Preface

by Dr Graham S Pearson CB

Porton Down has been inhabited for thousands of years as demonstrated by the excavation of a Bronze Age cemetery in the centre of the range by the Archaeological Section of the 160 strong Conservation Group of the Chemical and Biological Defence Establishment. Carbon dating has established that the remains date from about 1700 BC.

This booklet describes the first 75 years of Porton Down as the home of the United Kingdom defence centre of expertise in chemical and biological matters. The 7,000 acres of Porton Down within the Establishment are the jewel in the crown of the Ministry of Defence conservation. For example, at Porton Down there are more species of butterflies than anywhere else in the United Kingdom, the largest remaining tract of chalk grassland, one of the top stone curlew breeding sites and a major neolithic industrial flint centre. Preservation of the natural environment of this gem is a valuable side product resulting from the ownership and care of the 7,000 acres by the Ministry of Defence Chemical and Biological Defence Establishment.

In April 1915 chemical weapons were used on the World War I battlefield against the allied forces. This led to the requirement for a means of retaliation-in-kind and to protect the UK forces from this new weapon. This book describes how Porton Down was set up in 1916 and outlines its work in World War I towards providing a retaliatory capability and then how work continued in the inter-war years into both offensive and protective capabilities. World War II saw the creation of the separate Biological Department, Porton located on the Porton Down site and charged with the responsibility of examining the feasibility of biological warfare and of having a means to retaliate-in-kind should biological weapons be used by the Axis against UK forces.

Neither chemical nor biological weapons were used against UK forces in World War II. Subsequent years saw the priority for the biological weapons programme raised to that of the nuclear programme and then in the late 1950s all offensive work on chemical and biological weapons was stopped. The capability to retaliate to a biological warfare attack, using cattle cakes impregnated with anthrax against the cattle of Germany, had been destroyed shortly after the end of World War II and the chemical weapons capability and stockpile were likewise destroyed in the late 1950s.

Since the late 1950s, the role of Porton Down has been to ensure that the United Kingdom armed forces are provided with effective protective measures against the threat that chemical or biological weapons may be used against them. The fruits of this work were vital to the UK contribution to the coalition forces in the Gulf conflict in late 1990 and early 1991.

Fortunately, Iraq did not use either chemical or biological weapons and our equipment was not put to the test. Nevertheless, the Gulf conflict provided a timely reminder of the vital importance of ensuring that the armed forces are able to maintain their operational effectiveness even if chemical or biological weapons are used against them.

In its 75th year the Establishment changed its name yet again to the Chemical and Biological Defence Establishment thereby reflecting more accurately the role of the Establishment to provide effective protective measures against the threat of chemical or biological weapons. The Establishment also became a Defence Support Agency and as such is looking forward to the challenge of the next 75 years. Although CBDE Porton Down is doing all it can to assist the chemical and biological arms control negotiations, it is realised that arms control alone may be insufficient to deter a State from considering and possibly acquiring and using chemical or biological weapons. An essential pillar for the foreseeable future will be the maintenance of effective protective measures thereby significantly reducing the military utility and the range of chemical and biological warfare agents available to a potential aggressor.

The technical challenge of providing effective protection against the CBW spectrum and thereby ensuring that the UK Armed Forces can survive and maintain their operational effectiveness in a chemical or biological environment is a stimulating one. The strength of the multidisciplinary teams at Porton Down have been clearly demonstrated over the past 75 years, as has the essentiality of maintaining and improving the skills and capabilities of the staff to meet the requirements of the Armed Forces in a changing world.

GRAHAM S PEARSON
Director General CBDE

14 February 1992

The central area of the Establishment today: the 1918 Headquarters Building is in the foreground.

Lieutenant Colonel A W Crossley
CMG CBE DSc LLD FRS RE in
1918 painted by Lieutenant C A C
Stainer RGA and presented to
Crossley by his fellow officers at
Porton.

Porton Down

75 Years of Chemical and Biological Research

Introduction

1991 was the 75th Anniversary of the setting up of the hutted laboratories and the associated 'experimental ground' on Porton Down in 1916 to study the methods of chemical warfare and defence, in response to the first use of gas by the German Army. The first retaliatory attacks by the British had already been made, bringing the realisation that enthusiasm had to be tempered by study and experiment: hence the acquisition of the ground at Porton. Last year was the 51st Anniversary of the setting up at Porton of a group to study the methods of biological warfare in response to the threat of Axis powers use of this then largely unknown and unstudied method of war.

This booklet summarises three quarters of a century of Porton's preoccupation with chemical matters and half a century of activity in biological matters. It is intended to be intelligible to a diverse readership with many differing levels of knowledge about chemical and biological warfare and varying familiarity with Porton, as well as being of interest to any other reader. It will also provide an account of the history of Porton for the present staff of the Establishment.

Given that over 75 years have elapsed since the Establishment first appeared, there is a paucity of openly available literature on the history of activities at Porton. The first such major account is the Commandant's 1919 report on Porton during the Great War of 1914–1918: this document, known as the 'Crossley Report' is now in the Public Record Office, together with several thousand earlier reports from Porton. The second major work is the 1960 'A History of Porton' by an old Portonian, Lieutenant Colonel A E Kent, covering the period from 1916–1960. Known as 'Kent's History', it has recently been deposited in the Public Record Office. It was abridged in 1960 and this shortened version was published as a Restricted booklet in 1961 entitled 'A Brief History of the Chemical Defence Experimental Establishment, Porton'. It was de-classified to unlimited status in 1987 and put in the Public Record Office. These three key documents provide the backbone of historical data up to 1960. After 1960, the story of Porton has had to be assembled from reports, files and anecdotal sources.

Any account of Porton's past is interwoven with the sometimes complex history of chemical and biological warfare. Chemical and biological warfare have, in the past, been seen as quite
separate entities for some purposes: at other times they have been
much interwoven and they have many similarities. Many readers
may therefore be helped by the inclusion of an Appendix on the
nature of chemical and biological warfare. One further clarification
may be helpful: this booklet is not about a single Porton Establishment but largely about two distinct entities, albeit that for a decade
they were co-located and for a further near three decades,
adjacent. As far as possible the descriptions of events and activities
in this booklet use the titles which were extant at the time: where
no ambiguity arises, the term Establishment or Porton is used. The
media have traditionally failed to discriminate between the several
bodies and Establishments at Porton: this is not surprising because
there are complex aspects of Porton. For most of the past Porton
has had two and briefly three distinct defence Establishments.
These were all once a part of a large Directorate with a London-
based headquarters and further outposts at Sutton Oak and later
Nancekuke. Staff passed back and forth between the outposts and
the headquarters and sometimes also to India, Australia and
Canada. Some clarification emerges if the successive titles for the
major Establishments at Porton are set out chronologically.

Titles for the chemical warfare[1] or chemical defence area

War Department Experimental Ground   1916
Royal Engineers Experimental Station   1916–1929[2]
Chemical Warfare Experimental Station (CWES) 1929–1930[2]
Chemical Defence Experimental Station (CDES) 1930–1948[2]
Chemical Defence Experimental Establishment
    (CDEE)   1948–1970
Chemical Defence Establishment (CDE)   1970–1991
Chemical and Biological Defence Establishment
    (CBDE)   1991

Titles for the biological warfare[3] or biological defence areas

Biology Department, Porton (BDP)   1940–1946[4]
Microbiological Research Department (MRD)   1946–1957[5]
Microbiological Research Establishment (MRE) 1957–1979[6]

In 1979, when the Microbiological Research Establishment closed, CDE became responsible for both Chemical and Biological defence.

The former MRE building became the Centre for Applied Microbiology and Research (CAMR) in 1979 as part of the Public Health Laboratory Service (PHLS) within the Department of Health and unconnected with the Ministry of Defence.

Finally, there was for a time a separate Porton Establishment known generally as the Farm. The present CBDE animal breeding unit and the farm comprised from 1949–1973 a distinct Establishment of successively the Ministry of Supply, the War Department and the Ministry of Defence, known as Animal Farm, Porton and from 1954 as Allington Farm, Porton and with its own Superintendent. In 1973 Allington Farm became part of the then CDE. During the Second World War the supply of animals from Allington Farm was the responsibility of the Royal Army Veterinary Corps and the farm was briefly known as the Zoology Section.

---

1   Since the late 1950s Porton has been solely concerned with the provision of effective defensive measures.
2   In such times many official papers used merely the title. 'The Experimental Station, Porton'.
3   See footnote 1.
4   Located within the then CDES but as an autonomous unit.
5   Located initially within CDES as described above (4) but from 1951 as a geographically separate Establishment within a mile of CDES.
6   Merely a change of title.

A map from the 1919 'Crossley Report' showing the four stages in the acquisition of the experimental ground. A in 1916, B in 1918 and C and D in 1917.

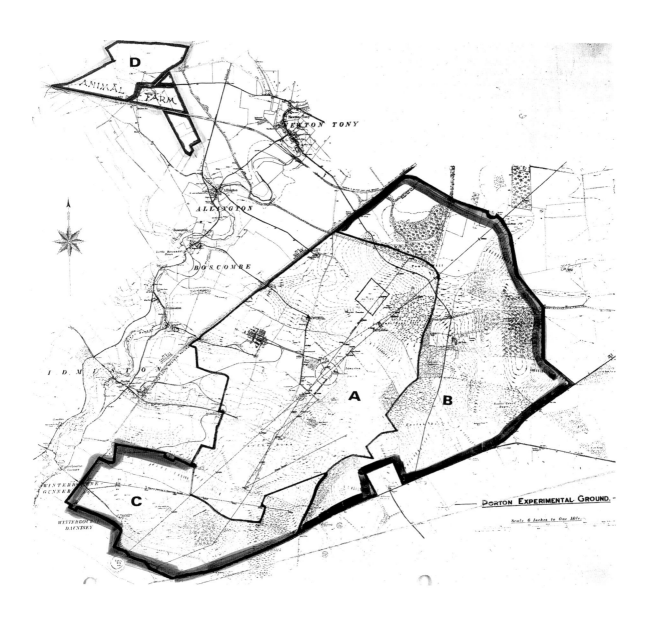

The Beginning:
The Great War of 1914–1918

I

Before the Great War, the Porton area was relatively untouched by the military activities which later spread over most of southern Wiltshire and especially Salisbury Plain, though on 8 September 1898, 50,000 troops assembled at Porton Down and marched to a review at Boscombe Down; an activity over then private land enabled by the recent Military Manoeuvres Act of 1887. Porton Down was not part of Salisbury Plain and was separated from it by the railway. The owners of land at Porton were numerous and seemingly ever-changing: they included Lord Normanton, Lord Nelson, the Countess of Portsmouth, Sir Harry Malet of Wilbury House, the Eyre-Matchams and many others. A few cottages, barns, farm buildings and, to the south, smallholdings were scattered over the chalk downs and the plantations. The only house of any size was 'Old Lodge', a 17th Century farmstead much restored in mid-Victorian days as a home for the Poore family and located four miles west of Nether Wallop.

The Poores were descendants of the family of Bishop Poore, who founded Salisbury cathedral in the 13th Century. Major Robert Poore was a prosperous and sporting country gentleman with a large family and an enlightened attitude to the conditions of

Old Lodge at some unknown time in the late years of last century. This pleasant early Victorian house of brick and flint was probably built on the site of a 17th century keepers lodge. When Major Poore moved in during the 1870s he demolished a chapel at the house and extensively enlarged the house to provide a gymnasium, Turkish bath and a laundry. It is unclear why the house was not used as accommodation or laboratories by the army in 1916. Reputedly, it soon fell into decay and was at times occupied by gypsies, until it was demolished in 1924 or 1925.

the Wiltshire farm worker. He had fought in India with the 8th
Hussars and retired from the Army in 1864. He was responsible
for the famous Winterslow Land Court which brought a form of
local government before the Parish Council Act of 1895 and
enabled the ownership of small plots. He became a Wiltshire
County Councillor and Justice of the Peace. Mrs Poore was one of
the founders of the now defunct Winterslow Weaving Industry,
later to become the Stonehenge Woollen Industries. All their seven
children are described as 'marrying-well', usually into the nobility
of the era. Perhaps the most unusual was Nina, the youngest, who
became Duchess of Hamilton and Brandon: she devoted her life to
animal welfare and founded the Ferne Animal Sanctuary at one of
the ducal houses, Ferne House near Berwick St John. In later life
she became the constant companion of the eccentric Admiral of
the Fleet Lord Fisher, whilst her husband, the premier peer of
Scotland, pursued a quiet life.

Events on the Western Front in 1915 were to bring great
changes to the Poores and to the tranquil rural life of Porton. On
22 April, the Algerian Division of the French Army was attacked at
Ypres, when the Germans discharged about 150 tons of chlorine
from 6000 emplaced cylinders over a front of nearly four miles.
The effects were devastating. Those who were not suffocated,
quickly broke from their lines and fled; the front collapsed. On 24
April the now uncovered flank of the 2nd Canadian Brigade was
similarly attacked. The first British troops to experience German
'gas' were the 1st Battalion of the Dorset Regiment on 1 May. On
23 April, Sir John French the British Commander-in-Chief
reported the first German attack on the French troops and urged
the War Office that 'immediate steps be taken to supply similar
means of most effective kind for use by our troops'. Retaliation-in-
kind and the means of defence were immediate needs: Sir John
also signalled 'Also essential that our troops should be immediately
provided with means of countering enemy gases . . .'.

The complexity of the subsequent British and Allied reaction
involved many areas beyond Porton Down, such as the chemical
industry, the Ministry of Munitions, the Royal Society and the
Services. Defensive matters were largely the concern of the
Anti-Gas Department in London, located mainly at the Royal
Army Medical College until May 1917. The matter of retaliation
was initially allotted to the Scientific Advisory Committee of the
Ministry of Munitions. Consideration of which gas might be used
by Britain was constrained both by industrial capabilities and the
lack of a suitable area for tests on a realistic scale. Some cylinders
were discharged in a trial on 4 June at the Castner-Kellner works

at Runcorn and the first British consignment of chlorine was sent to France on 10 July 1915. The charging of agents into shell and grenades and Service requirements were also discussed but it became clear that the reality of the British response awaited the provision of 'a ground for experimental purposes'. In September 1915 the Director General of the Trench Warfare Department nominated an officer to serve his Department's new Scientific Advisory Committee by finding a suitable place. Many sites were visited; in the interim some trials involving the discharge of hydrogen sulphide from cylinders had been done at Cannock Chase in December 1915.

Sites in Dorset, Suffolk, Hampshire and Wiltshire, including some in the neighbourhood of Andover, Netheravon, Stonehenge and Porton were visited by Professor H B Baker FRS, and then on 9 January 1916 by other members of the Committee. They recommended that steps be taken to acquire the Porton site and in the next few months an initial 2886 acres of the land near Porton was acquired from several of the owners. By 1918, further necessary extensions had resulted in the acquisition of Old Lodge and areas to the north-east and east, and the creation of Porton South (in the area now occupied by the Defence NBC Centre at

Gas casualties in the Great War. This sort of scene evoked John Singer Sargent's well known and emotive painting 'Gassed', which hangs in the Imperial War Museum. The reality was often less grim: these soldiers, though probably suffering intense and incapacitating conjunctivitis from the effects of mustard gas vapour, would usually have recovered from their temporary blindness and be fit for duty in about two weeks. During the whole of the war only ten British soldiers had subsequent persistent impairment of vision because of mustard gas and only few sustained injury sufficient to need removal of an eye. Mustard gas, though understandably potentially lethal, was primarily a long-term incapacitating agent. In terms of non-lethal but troublesome casualty production it was indeed the 'King of Gases'.

Porton Camp from the north in 1917. 'Gas Wood' is in the central middle distance. Though it cannot be seen in this reproduction, a football match is underway between the wood and the Camp.

Winterbourne Gunner) to a total of 6196 acres with a further separate 310 acres on the north side of the Amesbury and Military Camp Light Railway at Arundel Farm, a few miles west of Newton Tony.

The site was first described as 'The War Department Experimental Ground, Porton'; the appellation of Porton has remained though the site is rather nearer to the village of Idmiston and Idmiston Down. In the years before the existence of a road (constructed in 1924–1925) between Porton village and the London road, the main entrance to the Establishment was at the Idmiston railway bridge. Later in 1916, the title 'Royal Engineers Experimental Station, Porton' was adopted, reflecting the contemporary dominance of the Royal Engineers in British chemical warfare. On 7 March 1916 Sergeant Major Dobbs of the Royal Engineers reported for duty at the Experimental Ground. It is not clear whether there was anyone at Porton to report to; possibly he actually reported to the headquarters of Southern Command (which was then at Radnor House in Salisbury, on the site now largely occupied by the roundabout at the junction of the Wilton and Devizes roads) before taking the train or being driven out to Porton. On 16 March notification was received that 100 industrial-type cylinders containing hydrogen sulphide had been prepared at Oldbury, Birmingham under the supervision of Professor John Cadman of Birmingham University, a member of the Chemical Sub-Committee of the Scientific Advisory Committee of the Ministry of Munitions. After being transported by rail from Birmingham the cylinders (circa 5 feet long, 8 inches in diameter and weighing when full nearly 60 kilogrammes) were moved from Porton railway station to the experimental ground by local civilian labour, a slow and difficult process on account of the absence of proper roads. The cylinders were stored in what became known as 'Gas Wood' near the central bowl of the range and a night watchman was engaged to guard them.

Two large army huts had arrived on the ground on 30 March, one for an office and the other for a store. At the time it was thought that these were all the huts that would be needed at Porton but by May the Chemical Advisory Committee (formerly the Scientific Advisory Committee) of the Trench Warfare Research Department presented its view that the Porton ground should be put on a more effective basis and that £4000 should be spent on roads, fencing and workshops. Meanwhile, Sergeant Major Dobbs had been joined by Lieutenant Murray of the Royal Engineers as Officer in Charge of Works, to supervise constructions by the gang of thirty workmen; a body which may be seen as the forerunner of the Porton Works Department, the Ministry of Works, and latterly the Property Services Agency; branches which have looked after the fabric of the Porton campus over the years. Such work only proceeded rapidly from January 1917 and electric power, a light railway and considerable workshops and general facilities were available by 1918. At the time of the Armistice in 1918, what is now called the Headquarters or Main Block was under construction as the administration building; plans for more permanent buildings were also being considered.

On 6 April 1916 six civilians trained in the use of the 'Proto' self-contained breathing sets from the mine rescue team at Hednesford, Staffordshire arrived at Porton: they were to take samples of the gas cloud as it passed from the point of discharge. On 11 April thirteen civilian workmen were 'sworn under the Official Secrets Act' to be trained by Sergeant Major Dobbs in opening the hydrogen sulphide cylinders. An open air laboratory for analysis of gas samples was set up in the corner of 'Gas Wood'. However, the weather remained unsuitable for several weeks with both the mine rescue team and the Committee being summoned and returning to their homes on several occasions. In the interim a few desultory experiments were done on the flammability of hydrogen sulphide and the effect of explosives on cylinders. A Professor Walker also sprayed chloropicrin from a cylinder by means of compressed air. However, the major experiment with 120 cylinders of hydrogen sulphide finally took place on 26 May 1916, when the gas was released over a hundred yards front upwind of a system of trenches. Rats in cages were exposed in these and in the open. The mine rescue team, protected by their self-contained breathing apparatus, sampled the cloud as it passed over them by opening previously emplaced evacuated Winchester quart bottles.

The trial was successful in that lethal concentrations were demonstrated at least 300 yards from the point of release. However, British interest in hydrogen sulphide was short-lived. Though lethal, it was dangerously flammable, corrosive to cylinders, too light to stay near the ground after release and possessed a distinctive smell at very low concentration, enabling early awareness of its presence. A mixture of hydrogen sulphide and chloropicrin was more acceptable; this was heavier and not so readily dissipated. This mixture, known as 'Green Star' was stockpiled in France in 1916 with the aim of a future surprise attack on a vast scale. In the interim about 75% of the cylinders corroded and 'Green Star' was all but abandoned as a chemical agent by July 1917.

The use of chemical warfare in the field was seen as a suitable new role for the Royal Engineers. Initially, four 'Special Companies' (so called to conceal their actual nature) were raised in France by the posting of suitable soldiers from other units, and men with scientific experience or qualifications, who were to be enlisted as corporals with special rates of pay. Major (later Major General) C H Foulkes Royal Engineers, was promoted to Lieutenant Colonel and was appointed Gas Advisor to the Commander-in-Chief of the British Expeditionary Force in France and Commander of what was to evolve into the Royal Engineers 'Special Brigade'. The first draft of two officers and eighty men reached Foulkes at St Omer on 18 July 1915; more appeared on 21 July. An experimental ground was set up at Helfaut and training commenced in meteorology, theory and the practicalities of gas cylinder deployment. Despite great problems in production of chlorine and the supply of cylinders, the stockpile grew. On 22 August a demonstration was given to twenty or thirty of the senior Generals of the British Expeditionary Force. The first British attack was by now fixed for 15 September. On 4 September 1915 the Special Companies that had finished training moved up to the front at Loos; all wore brassards of pink, white and green, colours which were perpetuated until 1979 at Porton in the mess tie. The battle was however postponed; in the interim some 5500 cylinders were emplaced. At 5.50 am on 25 September gas and smoke were released from the emplacements to roll steadily towards the German lines. Britain's retaliatory capability had been demonstrated within five months of the first German use of gas on the Western Front.

However, the Germans were by now moving towards shells containing chemical agents, giving greater precision and flexibility: Britain too needed to progress beyond emplaced cylinders. Despite some scope for experiments in the field in France, it was clear that real progress would not be made by Britain until options were properly evaluated by scientific means. Such evaluations at Porton started in May 1916 and continued intensively. The results of trials and studies during the Great War at Porton were reported mainly by the publication of 7798 reports under the aegis of the Colonel Commandant Porton: these are now in the Public Record Office at Kew.

Foulkes was by no means a Porton man. He was offered and declined the post of Commandant at Porton after the war, but in 1919 he became a member of the Holland Committee which made profound recommendations on the future of chemical warfare and of Porton. Foulkes continued to serve in the Royal Engineers and returned briefly in his retirement to serve on the Weapons Committee of the Chemical Defence Board during the Second World War. He died in 1969 in his 95th year, doyen of the Colonels Commandant of his regiment and also father of a Colonel Commandant.

The outstanding figure at Porton during the Great War was its Commandant, Lieutenant Colonel A W Crossley FRS. Before 1916, Arthur Crossley, a Mancunian, as Professor of Organic Chemistry at Kings College, London, had been a distinguished academic and chemist, drawn into war work under the aegis of the Royal Society, initially as Secretary of the Chemical Sub-Committee of the Royal Society's War Committee, and then of the Scientific Advisory Committee of the Ministry of Munitions. In June 1916 Crossley was appointed to the post of Commandant and Superintendent of Experiments at Porton. He had been appointed Liaison Officer for Chemical Warfare, with the rank of Lieutenant Colonel in November 1915 and had spent some time in France. When Crossley arrived at Porton he found Sergeant Major Dobbs and Lieutenant Murray, two army huts with no roads leading to them, no water and no equipment. Within the month a chemistry laboratory was active in one of the huts: from the moment Crossley arrived work was done all day and most of the night.

In 1918, after the Armistice, Arthur Crossley was appointed Daniell Professor of Chemistry at Kings College and retired to the college on demobilisation in October 1919. In 1920 he turned to organising the British Cotton Industry Research Association at what is now the Shirley Institute in Didsbury. He received many honours from the State, the Royal Society and the Chemical Society before he died in 1927. The octagonal entrance hall to the headquarters block at CBDE has a brass memorial to Crossley; this was placed originally in the long-demolished hutted church at

The Porton Light Railway

The Porton Light Railway, a 24 inch gauge system, had five steam locomotives, one petrol locomotive and 150 carriages and wagons of several sorts. The railway started at sidings alongside the London and South Western Railway Company main line at Porton station and its eight miles of track ramified throughout the Station, the ranges and later to Porton South. The carriage of civilian workmen and fuel and stores to and from the main line Porton Station was a major role; it being the principal route for civilian labour from Salisbury. The light railway was still in use in 1951, though by that time the steam locomotives had gone.

Building the light railway 1918: this track is going south towards 'Gas Wood'.

The Winterbourne trestle under construction 1918.

Four steam locomotives.

the Establishment. A portrait of Crossley painted by Lieutenant C A C Stainer of the Royal Garrison Artillery, stationed at Porton during the Great War as the official 'Artist', hangs in the Director General's Office. The painting was presented to Crossley in April 1918 as a mark of the esteem in which he was held by his fellow officers at Porton: their signatures are on a commemorative address pasted to the back of the frame. In 1991, as part of the 75th Anniversary celebrations, the first of seventy-five trees, to be known as Crossley Copse, were planted at the Establishment.

There can now be few soldiers or civilians still alive who served at Porton during the Great War: our impressions of that period in the history of the Establishment come mainly from the 'Crossley Report'. Crossley was a keen photographer and the 'Crossley Report' is augmented by three large albums of half-plate photographs showing many facets of life at Porton under his command. These albums are believed to have been presented to the Establishment by the Crossley family in later years.

Crossley tells us that up to July 1916, civilian 'workmen' had been used extensively for experimental work, but on 5 July a detachment of nine NCOs and thirteen men of the Special Brigade Royal Engineers arrived as the nucleus of an experimental party. On arrival from Chatham at Porton Railway Station they were met by the military foreman of works and the village constable. Half the detachment were billeted by the constable in railway cottages and the rest in Idmiston village. The detachment paraded each morning at Idmiston church and marched up the cart track to the Experimental Ground. In September 1916 a series of major discharges from cylinders took place to optimise the techniques of sampling and analysing the cloud. As work progressed, and as German use of chemical warfare embraced the use of chemical shell rather than solely cylinders, it became obvious that experiments using artillery would have to be initiated. A special detachment of the Royal Artillery from Shoeburyness were used initially for this work, which started on 21 July 1916 with the firing of 4.5 inch howitzer shells charged with SK(ethyl iodoacetate; a powerful and one time standard British lachrymator named after South Kensington, where laboratory experiments were first done; probably at Imperial College) into 'Gas Wood' from what is now known as Battery Hill (then more usually known as Spion Kop because a private bungalow so named was earlier located there). Initial activity by the detachment had revealed inadequacies and the recommendation was made that a permanent artillery unit be made available. Accordingly, in February 1917 the nucleus of what was to become the Porton Battery Royal Artillery arrived, with the

two-fold role of firing for experimental trials and for the proofing of gas shell. The tradition of a Royal Artillery presence at Porton continued until 1957, when the Battery was disbanded.

The 'Crossley Report' describes the work of the Station in great detail, the way in which it was administered and the diverse engineering and allied facilities which gradually arose. For instance we read that, at the time of the Armistice, in the Motor Transport Section there were thirteen touring cars, eight Ford vans, four 15 cwt lorries, four 13 cwt lorries; ten steam lorries, nine motor-bicycles, two ambulances, two charabancs and a wagonette. Horsed transport also abounded.

Because of the food shortage, agricultural activity was started on the Station in 1917. One of the earliest British sugar beet crops was produced: corn, root and hay were also produced for fodder for the experimental animals. Animals were originally accommo-dated at Porton Down Barn (at the foot of the present road from the 'Porton-Pheasant road' to Battery Hill). Unfortunately the noise of the guns on Battery Hill was found to interfere with the breeding of some species and a new 314 acre animal farm was started at Arundel Farm, beyond the boundary of the Station and a few miles west of Newton Tony. Goats were much used for experimental work since their respiratory volume resembled that of man; in 1918 some 560 were housed at the new farm. Medical and toxicological work became of increasing importance as the war progressed. Data on the lethality of gas in relation to both concentration and period of exposure were critical to a proper understanding of gas poisoning and its treatment. Many toxic substances were examined; some 147 are recorded as having been studied at Porton before the Armistice.

The first physiological laboratory was set up in the main camp in 1917 but was later moved to Boscombe Down Farm on the Range and much enlarged, only to be burned down in the summer of 1917 and replaced by several hutted laboratories. Mr Barcroft (later Sir Joseph Barcroft), the physiologist, was eventually assisted

The Royal Automobile Club Section at Porton: public-spirited car owners donned uniform to serve the Army. The windscreen of the central car carries the message 'RAC on war service'.

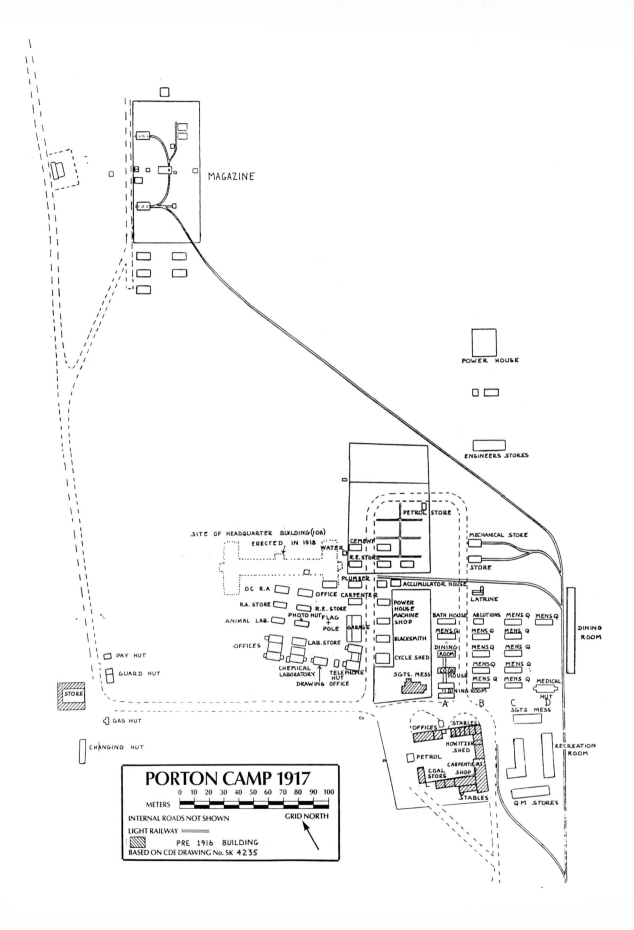

MAGAZINE

POWER HOUSE

ENGINEERS STORES

SITE OF HEADQUARTER BUILDING (106)
ERECTED IN 1918

PETROL STORE

MECHANICAL STORE

WATER

CEMENT

R.E. STORE

STORE

OC R.A

PLUMBER

ACCUMULATOR HOUSE

OFFICE CARPENTER

LATRINE

R.A. STORE

R.E. STORE

POWER
HOUSE
MACHINE
SHOP

BATH HOUSE

ABLUTIONS

MENS Q

MENS Q

ANIMAL LAB.

PHOTO HUT FLAG
POLE

MENS Q

MENS Q

MENS Q

DINING
ROOM

OFFICES

LAB. STORE

GARAGE

BLACKSMITH

MENS Q

MENS Q

CHEMICAL
LABORATORY

TELEPHONE
HUT

CYCLE SHED

DINING
ROOM

MENS Q

MENS Q

PAY HUT

DRAWING OFFICE

COOK
HOUSE

MENS Q

MENS Q

GUARD HUT

SGTS. MESS

DINING ROOM

MEDICAL
HUT

STORE

A

B

C
D

SGTS MESS

GAS HUT

OFFICES

STABLES

CHANGING HUT

PETROL

HOWITZER
SHED

RECREATION
ROOM

CARPENTERS
SHOP

COAL
STORE

STABLES

QM STORES

PORTON CAMP 1917

0 10 20 30 40 50 60 70 80 90 100

METERS

INTERNAL ROADS NOT SHOWN

GRID NORTH

LIGHT RAILWAY ▭▭▭

PRE 1916 BUILDING

BASED ON CDE DRAWING No. SK 4235

by Captain R A Peters RAMC (later Sir Rudolph Peters) who had experience of gas casualties in France. Other RAMC personnel were attached for special duties in the treatment of gas poisoning and to establish liaison with medical officers at casualty clearing stations and base hospitals. When the Anti-Gas Department from the Royal Army Medical College moved to Porton in 1917, cooperation with the physiology laboratory to explore individual and collective protection against gas became of great importance. This work was largely done by the then Captain H Hartley who was later appointed Controller of the Chemical Warfare Department at the War Office in November 1918 and, as Sir Harold Hartley, retained links with chemical warfare and defence virtually until his death in 1972.

Crossley describes how the work of the several departments was integrated, such as when an artillery experiment was designed to compare the lethality of the same gas fired from guns with different calibres required the involvement of the chemical laboratory to take and analyse samples, the physiological laboratory to provide and monitor experimental animals and to report on the clinical effects and pathology of the gas, the meteorological section, the Experimental Battery Royal Artillery for charging and firing of munitions, the Experimental Company Royal Engineers for trials organisation and layout and the deployment of volunteer observers, and the draughtsmen for observing and recording the fall of shell. Much use was made of the human observer who was unmasked but with his respirator at the ready, to act as the ultimate sensor and recorder of the effects on man.

Whilst much energy was devoted to offensive aspects of chemical warfare, the protection of the British soldier was a no less important matter. The first Anti-Gas Departments had been in London at the Royal Army Medical College and later at University College. Studies were also done at Bedford College, the Lister Institute, the Physiology Laboratories of Oxford University and the Central Laboratory in France. Following the first gas attacks, the immediate need was for the provision of gas masks (or 'respirators' as they became known).

Little other individual protective equipment emerged during the Great War, beyond impregnated leather gloves and linseed oil impregnated suits for occasional use by troops in areas where mustard gas had been employed. These items were not in general use however and the war ended before the particular problems associated with protection of the skin against mustard had been studied. The only other notable protective equipment to emerge was a cover for messenger pigeon baskets. Some desultory studies

Porton Camp in 1917.
The hatched buildings are those cottages and farm buildings which existed on the site before the army came to Porton.

Evolution of the Gas Mask

Within 36 hours of the first use of gas against the French forces, an improvised mouth-pad of some sort had been issued to all British troops. Improved impregnated pads or 'veils' such as the Haldane cotton waste-thiosulphate respirator followed in the early summer of 1915 but clearly the pad or 'veil' had limited utility. The idea of an impregnated flannel helmet with a mica window (the 'Hypo' helmet) was conceived, followed by the Phenate helmet and the Phenate-Hexamine helmet. Goggles were also produced to complement some devices. The more efficient and comfortable concept of an impervious facepiece with eye-pieces and the essential gas adsorbants and filters incorporated in an

The Black Veil Respirator.
The first respirator issued to the British troops in France in April 1915 after the attack with chlorine made by the Germans at Ypres salient. The gauze pad contained cotton waste and was soaked in a sodium thiosulphate (Hypo) mixture and protected against low concentrations of chlorine.

The 'H' Helmet.
Issued in early summer of 1915. The helmet was impregnated with Hypo and protected against chlorine only.

The 'P.H' Helmet.
Issued shortly after the 'P' Helmet. The hexamine increased the efficiency against phosgene.

In this respirator the outlet valve was introduced.

in World War I

attached container soon arose. It had the merit that any necessary specific absorbents for new gases could be added as a further layer in the container, a method not feasible with a fabric helmet. The first or 'Large Box' respirator issued in August 1916 had a container holding soda lime-permanganate granules, a facepiece of proofed fabric, mouthpiece, nose-clip and separate goggles. The facepiece was connected to the 'box' by a rubber tube. As with most respirators, numerous continuous improvements and modifications occurred, resulting in the eventual emergence of the 'Small Box' respirator in the later months of 1916.

The 'P.H.G' Helmet.
Issued in a very small quantity as the small box respirator was then being introduced.

The goggles were to protect the eyes against lachrymators which were introduced in January 1916.

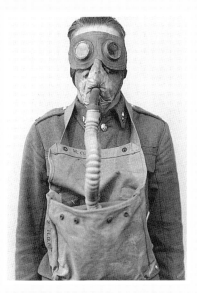

The Large Box Respirator.
This respirator was designed before the S.B.R. but had only a limited issue for special use, such as sapping and machine gun work. The large box gave a very high degree of protection and was found to be unnecessarily so for ordinary use in the field.

The Small Box Respirator. (S.B.R).
Issued early in 1916 and accepted as a general issue to all troops. Various fillings were employed in the box containers but in all cases charcoal was the main absorbent; granules of various chemicals were incorporated, sometimes mixed with the charcoal and sometimes in separate layers.

This respirator continued in use until the end of the war.

Gunners of the Royal Artillery during
the Great War.
One soldier is wearing the 'Small Box
Respirator'; his horse has some simple
prototype respirator. The soldier on
the right is demonstrating the 'alert'
position for these respirators.

on the use of fans designed by a Mrs Hertha Ayrton, widow of a
distinguished electrical engineer, to disperse gas from trenches
were soon abandoned. The respirators were generally made by a
large group of anti-gas factories in London and Nottingham set up
through the Contracts Branch of the War Office. The numbers
produced were vast eg 13,500,000 'Small Box' respirators and
14,000,000 Phenate Hexamine helmets: each 'Small Box' respirator had 105 individual components. At Porton, from 1917 the
Anti-Gas Department was primarily concerned with the collective
protection of troops in dugouts and trenches by means of blanket
curtains, and evaluation of British and foreign respirators in the
field under realistic conditions, especially the vulnerability of the
German respirator to British gases. Several distinguished scientists
and medical men were associated with the Anti-Gas Department
in London and later at Porton, notably Major (later Professor) E H
Starling and Lieutenant Colonel C Lovatt Evans (later Professor
Sir Charles Lovatt Evans FRS; who returned to Porton at the start
of the Second World War and again after his retirement in the
1950s). Another pioneer of early respirators was Lieutenant (later
Major) A Sadd who subsequently held senior civilian appointments
at Porton until the early 1950s. Others of the Great War who
subsequently served for many years at Porton in either military or
civilian capacities and who can still be recalled by some staff
included Lieutenant Colonel W A Salt, Lieutenant Colonel A E
Kent, Captain S J Steadman (at both CDES and MRD) and
Lieutenant A C Peacock.

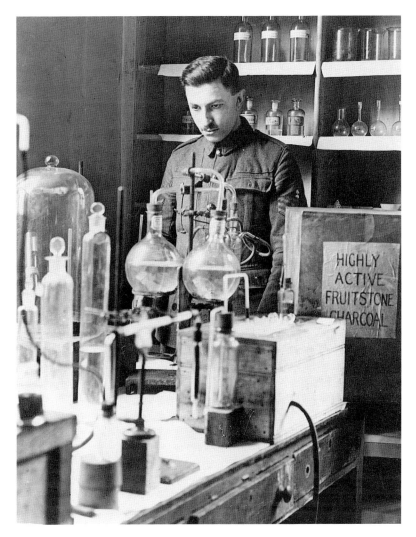

Research during the Great War. The provenance of this photograph is obscure and there is always a possibility that it records a scene not at Porton but at the Royal Army Medical College, or elsewhere in London. Nevertheless it is one of the earliest photographs of work on charcoal for respiratory protection. The identity of the NCO is unknown but he was almost certainly a Royal Engineer.

Crossley describes and illustrates the accommodation for troops at the Station; these were in the conventional military 'lines', eight rows of eight huts each accommodating 15 men. Other huts were provided for photographers, meteorology, the Medical Officer and the Medical Inspection room, the Labour Company Office, Sergeants' Messes and accommodation, the offices of the Experimental Battery Royal Artillery and the Experimental Company Royal Engineers, the Commandant, the Royal Army Service Corps unit, dining halls, kitchens, concert hall, fire brigade, recreation rooms, supper bar, canteen and bath houses. The Station generated its own electricity from a power house, backed by accumulators for lighting at night. Extensive machine and carpenters' shops, foundries and blacksmiths' shops existed, not only to sustain the self-sufficiency of the Station in repairs but in alterations and adaptations to shells and weapons and the construction of laboratory and field equipment. A magazine was originally set up in an old barn but towards the end of 1916, the increase in artillery trials led to the construction of a purpose-designed magazine on the site of the latter-day Officers' Mess. This was linked to the ranges by the light railway. In 1917, another magazine was set up at Porton South but by 1918 the numbers of shell in the main magazine, in proximity to the main array of huts, was causing some concern. Eventually after the war, a new magazine was built in a more isolated position on the range, where the present complex of Range Section buildings is located.

At the time of the Armistice, manpower at Porton was 916 officers and other ranks, 33 women of The Queen Mary's Army Auxiliary Corps, about 500 civilian workmen and the sole civilian scientist, Mr Joseph Barcroft. The officers messed at Idmiston Manor, not far from the main entrance to the Station. The women acted as typists and shorthand writers: an old photograph shows them posed formally outside their quarter in 'The Grange' at Hairpin Bend, Idmiston. This Corps (originally the Women's Army Auxiliary Corps) was disbanded in 1918. It was the forerunner of the Auxiliary Territorial Service and the Womens Royal Army Corps of the Second World War and after.

Hardly any vestiges now remain of the Station as it was in the Great War, beyond one of the stores buildings and the present headquarters building, designed by B F G Wakefield, who served

Ladies of the Queen Mary's Army Auxillary Corps outside their quarters in a house on the edge of the village of Idmiston during the Great War. Their shoulder-flash carries the earlier initials WAAC.

The Royal Engineers constructing the Headquarters Building in July 1918.

at Porton from 1917–1919 as 'Resident Architect' whilst with the Ministry of Munitions. This was under construction at the time of the Armistice and is now a Grade II Listed Building. Contemporary photographs show that most of the building work was done by soldiers of the Royal Engineers. The hutted 'lines' of the Great War remained for some years until new barrack blocks were built. Despite the vast numbers of civilian workmen, the military nature of the Station in the Great War is quite evident and indeed this continued for many years until the Army largely withdrew in the 1950s.

The discharge of gases from cylinders, first emplaced and then mounted in railway trucks or lorries, preoccupied the British for an untoward period. Grave shortages in the munition industry produced added problems and the United Kingdom was slow to follow German interest in the alternative means of delivering gas on-target by shells. Eventually we developed the Livens projector, a crude trench mortar, fired in batteries so that 'crash shoots' of several thousand projectiles or Livens 'drums' could produce an instantaneous and massive concentration of gas in the enemy lines. Firing trials with the Livens projector occupied an increasing part of activity at Porton, as did eventually the firing of shells. Particular technical problems were maximising efficiency of gas dissemination from the bursting munition, design of fuzes, minimising the decomposition of gas by the explosive forces, and the effect of ground temperature, wind and other parameters on the travel of the gas cloud formed from the burst of the munition.

More problems arose from the German use of shells charged with mustard gas in June 1917. The extraordinary vesicancy of this gas in both vapour and liquid form, its persistency on terrain and equipment and the effects on the eyes made this of great significance. Although not quick acting like chlorine or phosgene, mustard was relatively odourless and insidious. Casualty levels could not be limited by protecting the respiratory tract alone with a

The Livens projector.
The simple mortar displayed in this instructional photograph, was emplaced in batteries and fired electrically to deliver a 'crash shoot' of bombs filled with phosgene, usually with devastating effect, to a range of 1300–2000 metres. Nevertheless it was essentially a static weapon and laborious to deploy. Curiously, it persisted as an in-service weapon until the early days of the Second World War.

gas mask, since both vapour and liquid droplets exerted effects through the skin. The Station began a study of persistency, decontamination of man, equipment, houses and terrain. Bleach powder or paste was found to be a relatively simple decontaminant. However, it was evident that certain grave problems of protecting the feet, hands and body without serious physiological penalties and detriment of military efficiency, had to be solved. The war ended before these topics were addressed fully, although proofed leather gloves and boots had been evaluated. The development of defence against mustard gas was left for the inter-war years, as was the development of chemical warfare from the air and the study of its attendant problems.

The Armistice was celebrated with some enthusiasm by the troops at Porton; according to an autobiographical fragment by Sir Austen Anderson those in charge of the animals released a considerable number of monkeys; these reportedly frightened the occasional farm worker in the district over the ensuing weeks before eventually disappearing from sight. In recognition of Porton's role, King George V visited the Station on 16 September 1918. A few faded photographs remain to commemorate this visit. Crossley records that the Monarch 'observed some experiments'. Reputedly he was also amused by the chance discovery of a cake baking in a laboratory oven. Regrettably, the few known photographs of the visit are very poor, whereas most of the photographs of the Great War at Porton are of superb quality. Possibly the photographer, overcome by the grandeur of the occasion, had failed to estimate the correct exposure or hold the camera steady.

The visit of King George V on 16 September 1918. The King is escorted by Crossley.

The early years of the Station were pioneering in the acquisition of entirely new knowledge despite the exigencies of war and the inability to approach the matter systematically. There were clearly frustrations, particularly from the complexity of other departments beyond Porton concerned with chemical warfare (these have not all been mentioned much here but were essentially the Special Brigade Royal Engineers and the artillery on the Western front ie the users; the chemical industry, the munition industry, the Trench Warfare Department and the Royal Army Medical Corps). However, the Great War saw Porton lay down the principles for the study of chemical warfare and chemical defence, using the integration of the multi-disciplinary approach and evaluation under realistic field conditions. It also saw the accumulation of a unique database and the establishment of a permanent military facility at Porton. Indeed, until very recent times most local people used the term 'Porton Camp' to identify all or any of the distinct Establishments at Porton. The 'Silver Star' buses which served the Establishment and village needs for decades always carried the destination of 'Porton Camp' and there is still at least one finger post in the vicinity (at the cross-roads in Porton village) which carries this legend.

Assessment of the impact of the use of gas in the Great War on the Western, Eastern, and Italian fronts is difficult. Analysis of casualty figures is doomed to failure, because of a contemporary lack of definition and classification. Gas casualty estimates by several national official sources exceed a million but elements of uncertainty exist on the precise cause of death or major source of injury in those who were both gassed and wounded. Also, comparison of gas and other battlefield injuries shows vast swings in the proportions on different fronts in different years. Latter-day studies by L F Haber described in his 1986 book '*The Poisonous Cloud: Chemical Warfare in the First World War*' suggest that data on casualties, the cost of chemical munitions and their use, and attempts at a cost-effective analysis, lead to a dead end. The story of gas in the Great War on all sides is one of experiment and imitation conducted on a background of uncertainty and hurriedly assembled arrangements for both development, production and use. This was compounded by unfamiliarity and a lack of confidence, both to exploit gas warfare to the fullest and to seize the a initiatives revealed after successful attacks. Further, some methods of use were patently crude. The real utility of gas in the Great War cannot be determined. It brought no great victories yet it had an obvious military impact. Those who remained unprotected were vulnerable to the extent that all armies perceived the need to have

Mobile gas attack: a 1932 reconstruction.

Whilst the earliest use of cylinders was based on fixed installations, in the later stages of the Great War the 'Beam Attack' was developed. Here the cylinders, deployed in lorries or railway trucks were opened simultaneously to provide a continuous, cone-shaped 'beam' of gas which could penetrate, over a narrow front, deep into enemy territory.

A NCO of the Royal Engineers in the magazine compound at Porton during the Great War. He stands next to a 1650 lb 'SN' bomb, which were the largest such munitions of the period and known as 'bloody paralysers'. There is no evidence of the charging of such bombs with chemical agent, though aircraft bombing trials were planned at Porton in 1918 and at the time of the Armistice it was intended to conduct trials with larger bombs.

high levels of gas protection and, where possible, to develop and maintain the ability to retaliate-in-kind. The advent of mustard gas emphasised such needs. The greater impact was perhaps to evoke a level of public horror subsequently reflected in political concern of a magnitude sufficient to press for the very legality of gas warfare to be considered and for arms control measures to be applied. A major factor influencing both public and official minds was the apparent future vulnerability of the civil population to the use of aerial gas bombs in war.

In the Services, there were conflicting views on the matter of chemical weapons. Some senior officers were for the urgent development of gas warfare as an essential in future wars: others were less convinced, although conscious of the possible penalties of non-possession. Some thought that problems of defence were so great that no consideration should be given to any use of gas in future wars. This view probably arose because of fears that military scientists might de-stabilise conventional military doctrine to the extent that the conventional means of war familiar to the professional soldier would be subsumed in the still unconventional gas warfare. Equally, those with personal experience of gas in the trenches had other and humanitarian reasons for setting their faces against the further development of these means of war. Emotive assessments were undoubtedly made. The enthusiasts for the chemical arm pressed the alternative humanitarian view that short-term incapacitation from chemicals was the rule, rather than death and that, apart from the deaths associated with the early cloud attacks against unprotected or poorly protected troops, gas warfare had not resulted in a large proportion of casualty deaths. J B S Haldane in a now rare 1925 book '*Callinicus: a defence of chemical warfare*' states 'that of the 150,000 British mustard gas casualties less than 4,000 (1 in 200) became permanently unfit'. (He also describes in this little volume how 'someone placed a drop of the liquid on the chair of the Director of the British Chemical Warfare Department. He ate his meals off the mantelpiece for a month'.) Meanwhile, at Porton a sense of anti-climax prevailed.

The Inter-War Years 1919–1939

2

Uncertainty, Consolidation and More Uncertainty

At the Armistice, Porton was controlled by the Chemical Warfare Department, set up in 1917 with its headquarters in London, supporting the Chemical Warfare Committee and the Chemical Designs Committee (concerned with offensive equipment and munitions) and in addition to Porton, an anti-gas section at University College London, a research and small-scale experimental station at Wembley, and small units within many universities and scientific institutes. At Porton a massive exodus occurred. Soon, Service personnel numbers were reduced to skeleton levels and activity quickly expired in the face of lack of staff and uncertainty about the future role of the Station. Eventually, it was decided to shut down all parts of the Department except the London headquarters and Porton. The Chemical Warfare Department was transferred from the Ministry of Munitions to the War Office on 1 July 1919 where it became subordinate to the Director of Artillery under the Master General of the Ordnance, where it remained until 1939. Crossley spent some early part of 1919 writing the 'Crossley Report' but made no recommendations therein as to the future course of research, nor indeed did he refer at all to the future of Porton or of gas warfare.

In May 1919 a committee under the chairmanship of Lieutenant General Sir Arthur Holland was set up to investigate and report on the organisation of chemical warfare and to make recommendations on the needs of peacetime research at Porton. Its report was to chart the next 20 years: one practical import was the end of separate offensive and defensive research and development. The Cabinet agreed the suggestions from the committee and decided that research was to continue at Porton pending any decision by the League of Nations on the legitimacy of chemical warfare and on disarmament, and the subsequent level of United Kingdom accord with the international consensus. This decision, in 1920, led to a slow programme of new building at Porton, the reconstitution of the Chemical Warfare Committee and the gradual recruitment of civilian scientists. Married quarters, officers' and NCOs messes, barracks, a Commandant's residence, laboratories, workshops, gas chambers and experimental munition filling plant were built during the 1920s. What has for years been termed the 'Closed Area', to the immediate north-west of the headquarters building became the new focus for most of the scientific and technical buildings. The married quarters formed a parallel area outside the enclosing fence whilst the barracks were sited to the north-east. Throughout the 1920s most of the hutted lines of the Great War disappeared. The buildings at the Establishment are of interest, though largely utilitarian. Amazingly there are over 400; they vary from the elegant colonial facaded headquarters building to utilitarian brick boxes. Some have a certain quality or even charm. The 1937 building currently housing parts of the Medical and Biology Division is of that military architectural style of the period, sometimes called 'Hore-Belisha', after the one-time Secretary of State for War. The 1922 chemistry laboratory, now a store and in 1992 awaiting demolition, is plain and industrial with tall rooms and herring-bone roof windows resembling those of factories of the period. Perhaps most intriguing is that which now houses part of the Detection and Aerosol Division, but was built in 1927–28 as the Offensive Munitions Section. This briefly held title was soon changed to Technical Chemistry Section. The building, with its grey walled cloisters surrounding a central lawn has more than a faint monastic appearance. The engineering and other workshops of the Station reflected its manifold needs, the geographical isolation and the urge to attain self-sufficiency. In the Great War, many soldiers had manned the workshops; later, for reasons which have not been much investigated, the main engineering workshops were largely staffed by naval ratings, both artificers and seamen together with officers from the Corps of Naval Constructors and an Engineer Lieutenant Commander. A 1921 photograph of the Armistice Day parade at Porton depicts this naval unit passing the saluting base.

Staffing remained something of a problem in the 1920s. Civilian scientists appointments were temporary and an element of uncertainty about the future prevailed. In 1922 there were 380 officers and men of the Services at Porton but a mere 23 civilian scientific and technical officers and 25 'civilian subordinates'. By 1925 the number of civilian staff had doubled. Many staff of the early 1920s had belonged to the short-lived body called 'The Chemical Roster', which appeared to be both newly recruited men or the residues of long-service Special Brigade Royal Engineer men, grouped on similar lines to armament artificers elsewhere, as a branch of the Royal Engineers, administered by the Experimental Company Royal Engineers (later the 58th [Porton] Company RE). The 'Chemical Roster' was disbanded soon after 1922 and many men were re-employed as civilians.

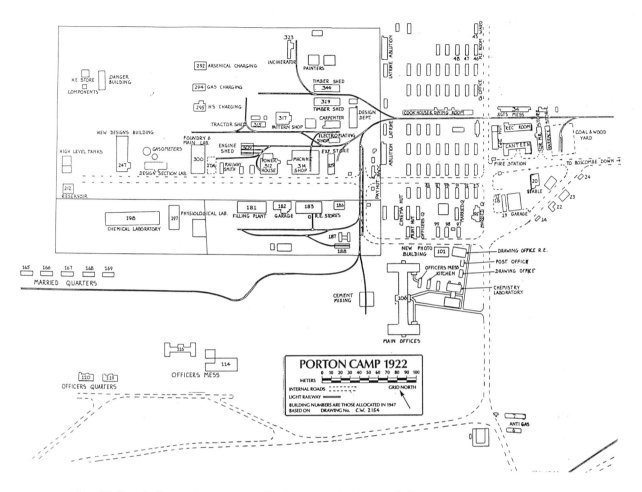

PORTON CAMP 1922

METERS   0 10 20 30 40 50 60 70 80 90 100

INTERNAL ROADS · · · · · ·   GRID NORTH

LIGHT RAILWAY ▬▬▬▬

BUILDING NUMBERS ARE THOSE ALLOCATED IN 1947
BASED ON   DRAWING No.   C.W. 2154

The Holland Committee report had stressed the need for fundamental research and stressed that this was dependent on attracting scientists of the right type 'Nothing short of £2000 a year could be relied upon to induce a man of the first rank to accept the post of Director of Research at Porton'. The general programme of research and development required was laid down in 1920 by the Services and the Chemical Warfare Committee. The main areas were individual respiratory protection, the collective protection of HM ships, the design of more efficient weapons and munitions especially aerial gas bombs, the meteorology of gas and smoke clouds and the treatment of gas casualties. The annual reports from 1921–1938, which were published successively by the Chemical Warfare Committee, the Chemical Warfare Research Department and (from 1930) the Chemical Defence Research Department, provide a detailed account of the progress of the programme at Porton, Sutton Oak[1] and in extramural studies. They also provide the definitive account of United Kingdom policy, doctrine

Porton Camp in 1922: the 'Closed Area' is now evident, as are married quarters and the Mess built on the site of the magazine of 1917.

and planning up to the Second World War. (These reports are in
the Public Record Office, in O and A papers WO33). The reports
lack great detail on all but the military and most senior civilian staff
and personalities at Porton. They do however provide meticulous
details of the membership of the Chemical Warfare Committee
and the subsequent Chemical Defence Committee, their associate
members and sub-committees. The outstanding impression from
such lists is the great eminence of those associated with the
Department and Porton in the inter-war years. Household names
in the world of science and medicine abound: Professor F A
Lindemann (later Lord Cherwell, Churchill's personal scientific
adviser during World War II), Professor R A Peters (later Sir
Rudolph Peters); H H Dale (later Sir Henry Dale); Lord Rayleigh;
Lord Rutherford; Lovatt Evans; Joseph Barcroft; J S Haldane; Sir
Harold Hartley; Sir William Bragg; Professor Perkin; Professor
A M Tyndall and many others. Regrettably, none of these reports
have descriptions of the fabric of the Station, nor of the way in
which day-to-day activity was pursued. In fact, there seems to be
no readily accessible means of picturing life at Porton in the 1920s
and 1930s. Anecdotes have been passed down the generations by
word-of-mouth but memories of the inter-war years and of the
Second World War, even amongst the oldest surviving retired
members of staff have all but slipped away.

The unpublished 'History of Porton' by Lieutenant Colonel
A E Kent, who formerly served in the Special Brigade Royal
Engineers in the Great War of 1914–1918, and later at Porton,
both in uniform (from 1919 to at least 1924 in command of 58
[Porton] Coy RE) and as a civilian until 1956, is probably the major
source of more parochial impressions. Kent, on his retirement in
1956, solicited a commission to write the history for £230. When it
was finished in 1961 the then Director of CDEE, for reasons
which are not now readily apparent, merely caused a summary
booklet to be written based on Kent's text. This summary was
prepared by C G Trotman when Head of the then Technical
Information and Records Section and issued in 1961 as a booklet
entitled 'A brief history of the Chemical Defence Experimental
Establishment, Porton'. This Restricted document was available to
an official readership. It was subsequently occasionally exposed to
a wider public readership by successive Directors and eventually

---

1   Originally 'HM Factory, Sutton Oak', then 'The Research Establishment,
Sutton Oak', and later the 'Chemical Defence Research Establishment, Sutton
Oak', this was the Department's process research plant for agent-production
studies until 1952. It was at St Helens in Lancashire and was resited at
Nancekuke in Cornwall from 1952 until its closure in 1979.

de-classified for unlimited access in 1987. As for Kent's large history, it was decided that it was equally unsuitable as an official history or, as Kent intended, a book for the general public. From 1962–1992 the typescript copies languished in the records of CDEE, where they nevertheless continued to be a major source of information. Kent's original introduction is worth paraphrasing: he writes that his history was aimed at a record of Porton's achievements, the process whereby civilians and servicemen had worked together, the national asset manifest in the unique facilities and expertise available not only for military purposes but for the civil sector, a record of Dominion and North American cooperation with the United Kingdom and finally to inspire 'those now serving at Porton and to those who come after, and to bring a pride of achievement to many, including those now retired'. The annual reports and 'Kent's History' provide some occasional snippets of camp life, including the 1921 complement for officers, NCOs, men, civilians of several categories and horses. The Commander and Adjutant were each allotted two horses, the Lieutenant Colonel (Chief Technical Officer) one, the RA Battery 64 and the civilian Director of Experiments one. The holder of the latter appointment was also privileged to receive eight weeks leave a year, though lesser staff could attain this level when ten years service had been completed. In 'Conditions of Employment for the Civilian Scientific Staff at the Experimental Station, Porton' it is intriguing to read that 'Private scientific work may be carried out by members of the staff in their spare time . . .' though 'No private scientific work is to be published without permission, which will not be unreasonably withheld'.

The scientific and executive staff at Porton in November 1928: the Director of Experiments, Mr N K Johnson, is sitting next to the Commandant. Lieutenant Colonel A E Kent, the author of an earlier history of Porton is seated sixth from the left. Several other veterans of the Royal Engineers Special Brigade appear in this photograph.

A Bombadier of the Royal Artillery in 1930, wearing the 1926 General Service respirator, with the Mark IV facepiece, as issued in 1927. The 'GS' underwent several minor modifications until supplanted by the 'Light Type Respirator' of 1942, which had the canister mounted on the facepiece, as does the modern S10 British respirator.

The 1929 Standing Orders for the Station give glimpses of military family life but little of that of the civilian staff. We read of the specifications for poultry runs in married quarters, when fuel, oil, disinfectants, bread, meat and groceries could be drawn from the Barrack Services and Supplies, how 'climbing onto hayricks or stacks for any purpose is strictly forbidden', conduct in the Officers' Mess, Post Office collection times, and the minutiae of military orders. Kent tends to relate minor events in ways reflecting a somewhat archaic sense of humour eg on the inadvertent aerial spraying of the married quarters with a dyed simulant and the discovery of a pink-spotted baby, Amesbury housewives dismayed by pink-spotted washing, the accidental destruction of a bursting chamber on the ranges, and japes during sea trials at Scapa Flow in 1923. Later, he is better with chapters on the 'Porton Home Guard' and the 'Officers' Mess: Social and Recreational Activities' which included bits on the Porton Musical and Dramatic Society and sports activities, notably the annual cricket matches between the Station and the chairmen of the many sub-committees of the Chemical Warfare Committee.

One of the major post-war tasks had been the assessment of the condition of a million wartime respirators. One per cent of the national stock was sent to Porton for penetration tests. The only convenient method was to do this by having men breathe through them whilst exposed to the irritant arsenical smoke DM (diphenylamine chloroarsine). These tests imposed some physical and physiological strain on the staff because the results were urgently needed and because the respirators were found to be largely penetratable and useless through deterioration. The deficiencies triggered Service requests for improved designs of respirators and the subsequent emergence of Naval and Army respirators and, by 1926, the common service GS respirator which became the standard pattern for the armed forces, until the 'Light Type Respirator' of 1942 largely supplanted it. Some 25 million GS respirators were produced before and during the Second World War, from the research and development of prototypes at Porton: all Commonwealth forces and much of the Air Raid Precautions (ARP) personnel were provided with this model.

Research into the protection of the hands, body and feet from mustard gas droplets and vapour during aerial attack was an important feature of the inter war years. During the Great War, the respirator alone had largely sufficed. Soldiers eventually learnt to keep away from splashed liquid mustard gas. In those years there was no prospect of a more insidious exposure to small droplets of mustard gas sprayed from aircraft. Mustard vapour was effectively kept out of the eyes and respiratory tract by the respirator. However, as the air forces of the major nations developed and the feasibility of aerial bombing attacks on cities grew, ARP became an increasing national concern. The use of gas under such conditions posed enormous problems. In about 1926, the study of this topic was added to the responsibilities of the Station. As a result of Porton's work, at the outbreak of the Second World War the country was very well prepared and equipped, notably in the provision of a cheap but efficient civilian respirator together with childrens and babies models, designed and developed at the Station for production by industry. Over 97 million of several types of civilian respirators were produced during the war. The United Kingdom was unique in providing such respirators, at no cost, to the whole of its population. (The actual cost to the Exchequer during the 1940s was about 15p in today's money for each respirator). It is significant that the first five ARP handbooks published from 1939 by the Home Office (but written at Porton) deal with protection against gas and the seventh deals with anti-gas precautions for merchant ships. Numerous other ARP memoranda and pamphlets were also largely written by anonymous Porton authors.

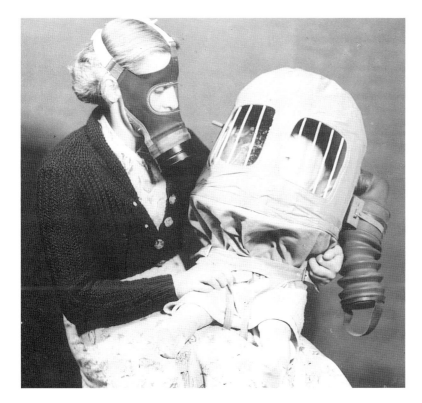

Prototypes for the civilian respirator and the baby helmet; 1938. Examples of such civilian gas masks can still be found in "antique" markets.

A 1938 trial to determine the droplet size of coloured simulants sprayed by aircraft on marching troops. Vertical and horizontal cards are carried by some soldiers who also have white sampling tippets on their shoulder.

Other products of Porton's research and development at the end of the 1930s include eye-shields to protect against high altitude liquid mustard gas attack (which would not be perceived and against which hazard the continuous battlefield wearing of the respirator would have been the impracticable alternative) the oilskin Cape Anti-Gas, impregnated battle dress (the treatment of fabrics with an 'impregnite' capable of reacting with mustard gas was a considerable research topic before and during the Second World War), protective dubbin for boots, detectors and detector papers and paint (for gas on equipment and terrain), sleeve detectors (a paper tippet or sleeve worn on the shoulder or upper arm upon which agent droplets would produce a colour change), heavier oilskin clothing for decontamination tasks, decontamination procedures and liquids, gas identification sets for service units, respirators and anti-gas covers for horses, mules and for war dogs. Protection for camels was also studied; a prototype respirator exists still in the Establishment.

There were probably no better equipped forces in respect of anti-gas defence than those of the United Kingdom in the late 1930s. We had emerged from the Great War of 1914–1918 with a respirator, techniques for gas-proofing dug-outs and buildings, and little else. At the end of the 1930s superior quality and scales of anti-gas equipment were available to the forces to cater for all known hazards. It is significant that during the Second World War the design of such equipment changed but little. Minor improvements were often incorporated from users experiences, or to reflect new threats. Occasionally during the Second World War inferior raw materials had to be utilised because of shortages; usually these were speedily replaced after Porton research on alternatives.

In summary, in the inter-war years, the anti-gas defence of the United Kingdom and its forces had been brought to a level which was superior to that of any other nation. The basis of this lay in the research and field trials done at Porton. The development and production by industry were masterminded by the Chemical

A Vickers Medium Mark II tank on the Porton Range in 1932 for trials on the vulnerability of tank crews to gas attack. This tank belonged to the 5th Battalion of the Royal Tank Corps. The 'plus-fours' glimpsed on the right appeared to have been popular with senior scientific staff for wear on the Ranges.

Prototype protection for army horses and mules 1938: a fragment of the Porton Light Railway is seen in the background.

Defence Research Department under the aegis of the Master General of the Ordnance. However, as far as offensive capabilities were concerned investment had been limited and production had been minimal in terms of agents and weapons, due to political unease and uncertainties. This situation was to an extent redeemed by the small amount of relevant research and development which Porton and Sutton Oak had been permitted to pursue during the inter-war years on the ways in which chemical warfare might be used against the British and Imperial forces in any future war. By 1938 the international situation was such that offensive research and development and the production of war reserve stocks of mustard gas were authorised by the Cabinet, albeit that it was realised that a useful production output could not be obtained for 12 to 18 months. The Italian use of mustard gas against Abyssinia in 1936 was a harbinger of concerns which steadily increased in the United Kingdom, especially since Italy was a state party to the 1925 Geneva Protocol.

The First Official Unease about Biological Warfare

It seems unlikely that any nation gave any serious thought to biological warfare until the 1920s. Before the latter half of the 19th Century one limiting factor was the lack of knowledge of the microbial origin of infectious diseases; though the concept of contagion was recognised earlier and many texts have cited archaic modes of biological warfare such as catapulting plague-ridden corpses into besieged cities in medieval times and distributing the bedding of smallpox victims to hostile North American Indians. In later years there was occasional speculation about the deliberate use of microorganisms in war and indeed reports arose in the Great War of 1914–1918 on German attempts at infecting allied cavalry horses with glanders. During the 1920s intelligence that other nations were beginning to take an interest in the potentials of biological warfare began to concern the Committee of Imperial Defence. The horror of gas which had arisen in the public mind during the Great War had combined with the urge for general disarmament to cause the League of Nations to negotiate the prohibition of gas warfare through the 1925 Geneva Protocol. During negotiations in the early 1920s Poland suggested that the prohibition on the use of gas be extended to cover 'bacteriological warfare' as 'an arm discreditable to modern civilisation'. The suggestion was readily accepted; although the subsequent states parties to the 1925 Geneva Protocol (often known as the Gas Protocol) can have had little real knowledge of the means whereby biological agents might be employed nor, indeed, any knowledge of feasibility beyond extrapolation from naturally occurring disease and medical microbiology.

Whilst the Geneva Protocol, which prohibited the use of chemical and biological agents in war, was a factor to be weighed in the minds of those who might otherwise have embarked in such use, it did imply to some that there might be military utility in such methods of war. Although there was an abhorrence of the concept, several nations recognised that they had to defend against it and some believed that possession of a retaliatory capability was a useful deterrence. Therefore, even though they eventually ratified

A 1936 trial to determine the effect of a harassing agent on the performance of a gun crew. In such times trials were realistic and involved the exposure of volunteers to agents under conditions resembling use in war.

the Protocol, several nations were stimulated into paying attention to biological warfare under conditions of great secrecy; as indeed they were quite entitled to do so, for the Protocol did not prohibit possession of the means of either types of warfare. Even the prohibition on use was a virtually a no-first-use agreement. Nations like Japan and even America which, at that time had not ratified the Protocol, were under no obligation to even conform to its spirit.

Increasing intelligence during the 1930s about German interest in biological warfare led to the War Department seeking advice from Porton, from the Medical Research Council and directors and deans of appropriate institutes and medical faculties such as Professor (later Sir John) J C G Ledingham, Director of the Lister Institute; Professor W W C Topley, Dean of the London School of Hygiene and Tropical Medicine and Dr S R Douglas, Director of the National Institute for Medical Research. Eventually, it was decided to formalise United Kingdom concern by the creation in 1936, of a Biological Warfare Sub-Committee of the Committee of Imperial Defence. The main influence behind this decision of the Minister for the Coordination of Defence was the Secretary of the Committee of Imperial Defence, Colonel Sir Maurice Hankey (later the first Lord Hankey), who remained a senior and controlling figure in the field for many years. The Sub-Committee, chaired by Hankey, included representatives from the medical services of the Royal Navy, the Army and the Royal Air Force, the Home Office and the Medical Research Council, several senior scientists from outside the official areas and the Chief Superintendent of the Chemical Defence Research Department Mr N K Johnson. Their mandate was to 'report on the practicability of bacteriological warfare and to make recommendations as to the countermeasures which should be taken to deal with such an eventuality'.

In the next four years the Sub-Committee prepared several major reports, mainly on defensive matters and notably on how vaccines could be made available. It was decided by the Committee of Imperial Defence in 1937 that the need for a capability for the United Kingdom to retaliate-in-kind need not be considered at present. A proposal to set up an Emergency Bacteriological Service was approved in 1938 by the Committee of Imperial Defence and the Sub-Committee was renamed the Committee of Imperial Defence Sub-Committee on Emergency Bacteriological Services, a move intended to reflect its defensive role. The name was then almost immediately changed; the existing title for the Service being thought 'too disturbing to the public mind'. At the suggestion of

A 1938 trial at Tipner Pond in Hampshire to determine the persistence of mustard gas on sand and shingle.

Two Hawker Audax and on the right a Hawker Hind at Porton in 1937. Aircraft for Porton trials were from the Special Duty Flight at Netheravon and later Boscombe Down. The title of the flight changed several times before 1946, when it was disbanded. Thereafter aircraft for Porton were operated on an ad hoc basis by 'B' Squadron at Boscombe Down.

Sir Edward Mellanby the title became 'The Emergency Public Health Laboratory Service' (after the Second World War the word 'emergency' was dropped and the Service continues today and indeed at Porton, where the Centre for Applied Microbiology and Research is one of the major centres of the Public Health Laboratory Service). The Service set up a number of laboratories, under the Ministry of Health but managed by the Medical Research Council; these became used for general public health work and still constitute the regional network of the Public Health Laboratory Service, some laboratories being located within hospitals and others existing as separate entities. Neither the Public Health Laboratory Service nor CAMR now has a biological defence role and their origins in such defence are mere matters of history.

Activity at Porton in the early months of 1939 clearly increased in intensity and pace. In August, the Establishment was transferred to the Ministry of Supply. The advent of war must have brought profound changes to everyday life at Porton, both for civilians and the military staff, yet there are virtually no comprehensive records available. The instructions and plans which inevitably must have been promulgated by the London headquarters and by the Commandant are no longer preserved at Porton. The files of the period lie in the Public Record Office but clearly much of domestic and parochial interest disappeared long before such archives left the Departmental Records Office for the Public Record Office. Many orderly room files of interest were destroyed when the major military presence left Porton in 1957.

The Second World War 1939–1945

3

The Prospect of Attack and Retaliation

There was a near-complete lack of chemical munitions at the onset of the war on 3 September 1939. No artillery munitions, Livens projector drums, mortar bombs, rockets or other devices charged with agent were stockpiled for Army use. A few 250 lb mustard gas bombs for the RAF, together with some 250 lb spray tanks may have been available, since charging started in August and September 1939. Some 500 tons of mustard gas and 5 tons of tear gas were available in bulk stocks. Had the Germans initiated chemical warfare at the outbreak of war, the immediate ability of the United Kingdom to retaliate-in-kind would have been negligible. The chemical warfare handbooks for the army of 1940 reflected the dated concepts and lack of chemical munitions for artillery; detailed instructions were provided on a the deployment of the cylinder, an essentially archaic chemical weapon. Fortunately, the defensive position was probably the best in any of the European forces. Provision of such equipment soon extended to the rapidly growing Territorial Army, to militia training and, a little later, to the LDV (Local Defence Volunteers, later to become the Home Guard). Overseas garrisons were reasonably well equipped and any deficits were soon made up. When Japan entered the war in 1941, the Imperial and Allied forces were faced with the prospect of using retaliation-in-kind and anti-gas defence on an almost world-wide basis. Japan was not a signatory to the 1925 Geneva Protocol and the Chinese had claimed that the Japanese Imperial Army had used chemical weapons against their forces on several occasions since 1937.

On 5 September 1939, two days after the outbreak of war, the Chemical Defence Research Department moved from Grosvenor Gardens in London to Porton, leaving a small rear party to maintain contact with the Ministry of Supply headquarters. By February 1940, because of difficulties in liaison with other departments the greater part of the London staff returned and were re-established in the Adelphi. Records and intelligence branches remained at Porton for some years; the latter returning to London in May 1943 and the former being absorbed by CDES.

Porton expanded considerably in the early months of the war, with an influx of scientists and technologists from the universities

The Chemical Defence Experimental Station at the start of the Second World War. Some of the hutted lines of the Great War period remain to the left and right of the barrack square at the right of the photograph.

and industries. The mechanisms are now somewhat obscure but plans had been made by the Government for certain key scientists to join defence establishments on the outbreak of war. Other such moves were instigated by the senior academics and industrialists on the Chemical Defence Committee. Many distinguished scientists worked at the Establishment for periods during the war, including Professor G R Cameron the pathologist (later Sir Roy Cameron); Professor S Sugden, Professor H W (later Sir Harry) Melville, Dr H M Carleton known to generations of histologists for his manual '*Histological Technique*', Sir Joseph Barcroft; C N Davies the doyen of aerosol research, Professor J H (later Sir John) Gaddum the pharmacologist and pioneer of probit analysis, and Sir Jocelyn Thorpe the eminent chemist. The actual number of CDES staff during the Second World War cannot be readily determined: it seems likely that total staff numbers were somewhere between 700–1000, including servicemen. Changes in organisation also occurred.

During part of 1940–41 there was both a military Commandant and a civilian Chief Superintendent. In August 1941 the Commandant combined both roles. By 1942 the title 'Commandant, Porton' had lapsed leaving the now military Chief Superintendent as effective head of the Station. This military post continued until 1948 when the title became a civilian appointment and eventually was re-designated Director in 1956.

On the declaration of war a London-based Territorial anti-aircraft gun battery was posted to Porton and manned several sites within the camp and on the range. In the event, Porton was never attacked. Many buildings were camouflage painted; the faintest residual pattern can still be seen on one or two buildings. Extra hutted living accommodation was built for the Officers Mess and for servicewomen. In fact, a rash of satellite huts appeared in all parts of the Station. Defensive pill-boxes were added to the corners of the 'Closed Area': these have escaped listing in a 1985 definitive published account; *'Pill-boxes: UK defences in 1940'* by Henry Wills, a local author.

As the war in Europe developed the British Expeditionary Force in France fully expected to be confronted by German gas. In such a situation, as on the home front, many incidents were reported and investigated. Porton was the vital part of the evaluation process. False alarms continued to show the need for any use of gas by the enemy to be properly established and authenticated. Perhaps one of the most notable scares was the very widely accepted notion that in the autumn of 1940 the Germans were releasing some form of vesicant threads or cobwebs into the air over the United Kingdom. The Home Guard and ARP wardens seemed to have originated this concern. Studies at Porton soon confirmed the immediate scientific impression that these were not sinister secret weapons but a harmless natural phenomenon. One of the files of the period contains a copy of letter LXV from White's *'Natural History of Selborne'* wherein the great naturalist describes similar unusual concentrations of airborne gossamer encountered on 21 September 1741; a poem entitled 'Gossamer' written subsequently by some unknown member of the staff at GHQ Home Forces (then at Kneller Hall) in September 1940 contains the lines:

> 'Security of home and health were shaking in their pants
> Till Colville quoted a piece from White of Selbourne, Hants.
> They sent it out on all the wires 'This matter's quite alright
> For any further references see letters, Gilbert White'.

The arsine scare was somewhat less ludicrous and based on tenuous intelligence. Arsine or arseniuretted hydrogen (code-named Arthur) was a lethal, non-persistent agent with a systemic effect in destroying red blood cells. The Germans had always been keen on arsenical agents, the German respirator FE37 introduced before 1939 had been found to give high levels of protection against arsine and it was also learned that in the immediate pre-war period Germany had cornered all the available arsenic on the world metal market. The juxtaposition of these matters lead to the

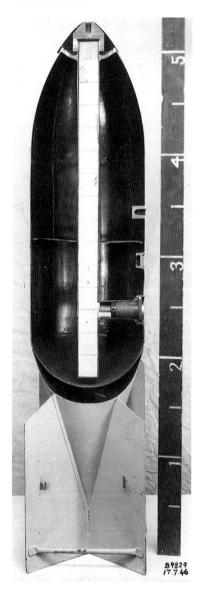

Inside the German 250 kg chemical bomb: this has been emptied and cut through at Porton to show the central bursting charge, the large void which was filled with chloracetophenone and the relatively thin walls typical of a chemical bomb.

assessment that arsine might be used against the British Expeditionary Force. An auxiliary respirator canister (the Type EA) filled with specially treated absorbent granules was quickly provided for the GS respirator, being inserted in the middle of the corrugated rubber hose which connected the facepiece to the main canister. A special Detector Paper Type A was also developed at Porton and rushed into service. Investigations after the war showed that fears had been unfounded. The high levels of arsine protection afforded by the German respirator were fortuitous (being aimed at countering the threat of Russian hydrogen cyanide), and the arsenic stocks were for more general industrial use. That part of the stocks which was destined for chemical agent production was intended for the production of arsenol, which the Germans used as a diluent for mustard gas. The lessons from such events were well learnt and by 1942 when similar scares about German use of 'Substance S' (HN_2, one of the nitrogen mustard series) arose, the matter was better handled and the highlighting within the Army of any special threat was avoided. The 'mirror-image' effect in the history of chemical warfare is well known and it is a salutary observation that the German perception of the sudden appearance of British detector paper for arsine, led them to assess that this gas must be a British agent of significance. This, in turn, led them to intensify their previously low level of interest in arsine.

Intelligence on the chemical warfare capabilities of the Axis powers was closely scrutinised at Porton and when the Chemical Defence Research Directorate headquarters returned to the Adelphi, its intelligence branch CDR5 remained at Porton until May 1943 under Major General Sir Henry Thuillier (Retd), who had been Director of Gas Services at GHQ in France and subsequently controller of the gas warfare branch of the Ministry of Munitions in the Great War. (Thuillier was the author of a 1939 book entitled '*Gas in the next war*' but which is curiously almost completely devoted to gas in the Great War. Unlike the situation in the United States America and Germany, there were very few openly available authoritative British texts on chemical warfare by former soldiers or officials, due to an attitude in the 1920s and 1930s that the public should not be disturbed by knowledge of the potential of gas in future wars. Open British publications, when they emerged at all, tended to appear in the medical literature).

All captured equipment was exploited in the laboratories and the fullest reports issued. The most commonly studied equipments were Axis respirators; special interest lay in the performance of the charcoals and particulate filters in the canisters in the context of their vulnerability or indications of new Axis agents. Capture of

A 1941 prototype for the 'Installation Type A/LP' or Bulk Contamination Vehicle designed for the contamination of terrain with mustard gas. The white paper squares are being used in a trial with a coloured simulant to detect the extent to which the vehicle itself becomes contaminated.

chemical munitions was a rare event until the end stages of the war; all possessing nations took care to prevent such munitions falling into enemy hands. Some British chemical weapons, mostly Livens projectors, which had been taken to France by the No 1 Chemical Warfare Group of the British Expeditionary Force, were lost to the Germans at the time of the British evacuation. Further, certain British experimental devices and reports which had been given to the French, were discovered by the Germans when they over-ran the French chemical warfare laboratories at Le Bouchet.

What were the major concerns in the chemical field at Porton during the war? Without doubt the greatest was to intensify the development of new chemical weapons and munitions; this had been started before the war in a desultory manner constrained by political uncertainties about retaliatory policy and compounded by lack of funds and resources. Hand-in-hand with this now accelerated development was the establishment of a section to plan and assess field testing and work with the operational requirements branches on battle-field tactics, munition expenditure and firing tables. Constraints on the scale of field trials at Porton were partly relieved by the collaborative efforts of Canada in setting up the Suffield Experimental Station in Alberta for conjoint use. Earlier Anglo-French plans to collaborate in trials at the French field trial facility in Algeria had foundered with the fall of France.

As the war progressed the number and range of chemical weapons and munitions which passed into service increased. By the end of the war in Europe the United Kingdom had appreciable stockpiles both at home and in theatres of war overseas. The United Kingdom's chemical agents, phosgene, mustard gas and a

A Fairey Albacore of the Fleet Air Arm engaged in trials over the Porton Ranges in the 1940s.
The aircraft is disseminating a dyed simulant for mustard gas from its SCI (Smoke Curtain Installation). The SCI could be used to disseminate smoke or chemical warfare agents and was one of the major British chemical weapons of the Second World War.

lachrymator (teargas: usually bromobenzyl cyanide generally termed BBC) were produced and weaponised in Agency Factories run by the chemical industry for the Ministry of Supply, under conditions of secrecy and urgency. This association of industry and the Chemical Defence Research Department, notable through the station at Sutton Oak, began in 1937. The main Agency Factory was at Randle in Cheshire; others were constructed at the Valley works at Rhydymwyn in North Wales and Springfields near Preston in Lancashire. Intermediates were produced at Rocksavage near Runcorn (which also produced phosgene), Wade near Northwich in Cheshire and Hillhouse near Fleetwood in Lancashire. Depots for bulk storage and ad hoc filling of RAF spray tanks were scattered throughout Britain: Army holdings of chemical munitions tended to be co-located with more conventional munitions. Between 1939 and 1945 3,394,093 Porton-designed 25-pdr Base Ejection shells charged with mustard gas were produced. In the same period impressive quantities of other calibre shells charged with one of the three standard United Kingdom agents were produced. For the RAF, bombs charged with mustard gas or phosgene and ranging from 30 lb to 500 lb were produced by the thousands. Nearly 60,000 spray tanks of various sizes were also produced. The total United Kingdom Second World War production of gas, both charged into munitions and weapons or held in bulk storage was 40,719 tons of mustard gas and 14,042 tons of phosgene and tear gases: the cost of such production was £24m. Apart from these Army and RAF munitions and weapons, shells for naval guns, mostly of 4 inch and 4.7 inch calibres were designed and trialled. Stockpiles of such shells charged with phosgene were laid down in shore depots but none were carried on

A curious chemical weapon of 1943; the frangible glass grenade. Many ideas were evaluated and discarded during the Second World War.

board HM ships. The only doctrine for naval use of gas shell was bombardment of land targets before or in support of landings. Whilst the naval stockpile was modest beside that of the Army and the RAF, a considerable development and trials programme at Porton was needed to fulfil Admiralty needs in an area where no real requirement had been stated until 1939.

Many experimental weapons and munitions were developed and trialled at Porton during the Second World War. Many were in response to Service requirements for chemical weapons specifically designed to attack armoured fighting vehicles, bunkers or pill-boxes. Others reflected efforts to increase the efficiency of aircraft delivery of mustard gas. Many such devices acquired local nicknames such as the 'Flying Cow', 'Flying Lavatory', 'Squirt' and 'Frankfurter'. None passed into service because the requirement lapsed due to changing circumstances in specific theatres of war, or as the European and then Japanese war periods drew to an end, because of the diminishing likelihood for a need to retaliate in kind against the Axis.

The search for new agents was another major concern at Porton. Much was also done by extramural work at Universities, notably at Cambridge. When promising, new, highly toxic compounds were identified, several were taken to the stage of laboratory-scale production for field assessment but largely by the time important new classes of putative agents had been identified, the war had progressed to the stage where the lengthy process of development, trialling, developing production processes and scaling up to bulk production, was not considered worthwhile.

Smoke had been studied at Porton since the Great War, for screening, marking and signalling. The Second World War led to urgent operational requests for new smoke munitions and devices of all sorts, especially in coloured smoke for signalling and also the means to screen exceptionally large vital industrial targets at home. The needs of the Royal Navy for generating smoke were long standing. For special operations such as the Dieppe raid, Porton smoke devices played a significant role, as they later did in the invasion of occupied France.

The possible retaliatory use of gas against the Japanese forces and the particular problems of defence against Japanese gas in tropical conditions was yet another problem of the period. The performance of impregnated clothing and anti-gas ointments under such conditions continued to be a weakness. Several agents, notably mustard gas, were more potent in tropical conditions. The development of an anti-gas ointment which would give skin protection against mustard gas for long periods in hot, sweaty conditions was eventually fulfilled by the development of Ointment Anti-Gas No 6.

The impregnated clothing problem was more difficult. The most-used British 'impregnite' (2.4 dichlorphenyl benzoyl chloroimide) was named Anti-Verm (A subterfuge suggesting some anti-louse or insecticide property, employed for security reasons to avoid drawing foreign attention to the existence of British battle-

Lord Louis Mountbatten watching a demonstration at Porton of smoke devices for possible use in the Dieppe raid. The date is not known but is probably the early summer of 1942. Air Commodore Combe, the Chief Superintendent skirts the unidentified senior officers behind Mountbatten. Lieutenant Colonel A.E. Kent, then Military Experimental Officer, is largely hidden by the Grenadier Guards Officer in the foreground.

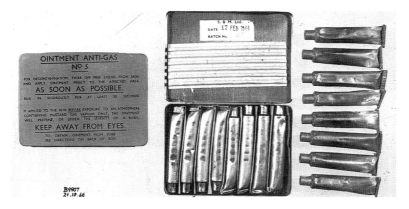

Ointment Anti-Gas No 5.
Two tins of ointment tubes formed part of the Serviceman's personal anti-gas equipment. The No 5 ointment contained 'Anti-Verm', di-ethyl phthalate, fish oil and soap. It both protected exposed skin against vesicants such as mustard gas and neutralised their effects.

dress impregnated with chemicals capable of neutralising mustard gas. Inevitably, the Germans came to know of such matters when the British Expeditionary Force left France and British Anti-Verm socks were acquired). Impregnated clothing concepts had been a considerable preoccupation at Porton since 1935 and of interest from at least 1925. By 1938 co-operation with the dry-cleaning and textile trades had enabled a process which could be used for service battle dress in a standard dry cleaning plant. Impregnated battledress worn with a respirator was seen as the ideal alternative to encumbering troops with heavy impervious oil-skin clothing which could readily exact a physiological penalty under hot weather conditions or with arduous activity. Protection of the hands and feet was still needed, but this was not a major problem. Foot protection was initially by impregnated socks but later by the use of protective dubbin on boots. Serge battledress impregnated with Anti-Verm was stable in storage under temperate conditions. Under battle condition use, the protective properties remained for about three months. Laundering and dry-cleaning destroyed the 'impregnite', so that a withdrawal and recycling process had to be instituted by the Royal Army Ordnance Corps, using special dry-cleaning firms. The scale of issue of impregnated battledress and, until 1940 socks, was impressive. All British and Commonwealth troops taking part in the invasion of occupied Europe were equipped with such clothing. Meanwhile, at Porton, thought was being given to the development of an impregnated 'pantee' to protect the vulnerable groin area; the special problems of kilted troops were also studied.

The utility of Anti-Verm impregnated clothing in the tropics was one of the topics studied by a conjoint United Kingdom-Australian team at the Australian chemical warfare laboratories and field stations at Prosperine and Innisfail in Queensland. It was

Low-cost protection from aerial spray of mustard gas: a 1943 American prototype. Defensive equipment from the Allies and the Axis nations was carefully studied at Porton.

found that under very hot and humid conditions the Anti-Verm was adsorbed through the skin to produce mildly toxic effects. This limitation and the difficulties found in impregnating lighter cotton fabrics led eventually to the adoption of American 'impregnites' and plant. When the war ended, impregnating companies were about to be raised in India, for which American plant was to be made available.

As the war proceeded, research on insecticides and repellants became important at Porton. The toxicology, physical properties and dissemination of DDT was given high priority from 1943. Impregnation of service shirts with DDT all but eradicated the perennial problem of lousiness in the field army: the first United Kingdom large-scale of production of DDT was at Sutton Oak. Medical aspects of war beyond those of chemical warfare were studied by Porton, including the effect of underwater explosions on immersed personnel, burn treatment, the hazards from explosive fumes in gun turrets, pill-boxes and tanks and from smokeless propellants.

With the advent of VE day, the trickle of senior staff returning to their pre-war posts began: the complement was cut by 10% and the Station programme revised. Inevitably, the future role of the Station began to be discussed, especially in the light of the fact that gas had not been used and the possibility that no nation had seen it as an essential part of military activity. Whilst discussions of such a sort continued in high places, they were disturbed by the British discovery in April 1945 of German chemical shells bearing unknown markings. Cautious examination of the agent charging revealed a highly toxic and (then) largely undetectable compound which could exert effects in a few minutes if inhaled or if the skin was contaminated. Further, exposure to non-lethal concentrations could produce severe and prolonged effects on vision. Subsequently this particular agent known to the Germans as Tabun or Trilon 83 was found to be but one of a series of related compounds which the Germans had termed the G-agents and which eventually became more commonly known as the nerve agents. Concern about possible chemical warfare in Far East theatres of war was relegated and almost the whole of Porton activity was now directed to investigation of the German chemical warfare capability, both by Porton and Allied scientists at the German chemical warfare facilities and when samples were brought to Porton for detailed study. A vast programme of work on the nerve agents was mounted, both within Porton and extramurally with eminent contacts such as Professor Adrian (later Lord Adrian PRS) at the University of Cambridge.

During the few remaining months before V J day, vigilance about a possible Japanese last-minute use of chemical warfare was maintained in the face of fastly-depleting staff, studies on the nerve-agents and the inevitable uncertainty about the future role of Porton. Gas had not been used; what then was its place in future wars? Had the nerve agents brought a new dimension to chemical warfare? What were the implications for any United Kingdom chemical warfare capability of the future? How were the new problems in defence, notably detection, prophylaxis and therapy to be solved? What was the impact of the nerve agent hazard on British military doctrine? Clearly, one of the major post-war tasks was to evaluate the German nerve agent munitions in the field.

The Second World War had seen great activity at Porton and by Porton workers dispatched to India, Australia, Canada, South Africa and the United States. The United Kingdom retaliatory capability had been developed after pre-war inertia and the means of defence improved. Undoubtedly these states of United Kingdom and Allied prepardness against possible Axis powers use of gas did much to influence the Axis decision not to use their considerable chemical warfare capability. Thus, the view emerged that the Allies infact had won the gas war, without either side having recourse to this particular method of warfare.

Concepts of Biological Warfare put to the Test

The advent of the Second World War, intelligence on more suspect activity in Germany, discussions with the Medical Research Council and communications with Sir Frederick Banting of Canada (one of the discoverers of insulin) caused the Committee of Imperial Defence to re-convene its original Sub-Committee on Biological Warfare. By February 1940, again under the Chairmanship of Lord Hankey, as Minister Without Portfolio in Chamberlain's War Cabinet, this became the War Cabinet Sub-Committee on Biological Warfare. The main need identified by the new Sub-Committee was for concepts to be devised and put to the test of experiment. In April 1940, the Sub-Committee was informed about exploratory work by France and in June Sir John Ledingham reported on work on inhaled toxins by Dr D W W Henderson, a member of the staff of the Lister Institute. By September discussions between the Ministry of Supply and the Medical Research Council had resulted in arrangements for setting up at Porton a highly secret group to undertake a practical evaluation of biological warfare. This small group was to be co-located with CDES. It would rely on the many facilities and experience of the Station but would remain autonomous under its Director Dr Paul Fildes (later Sir Paul). Fildes reported initially to Lord Hankey as Minister without Portfolio and later to Mr Duff Cooper as Chancellor of the Duchy of Lancaster, though some token service involvement emerged later through the emphemistically titled 'Porton Experiments Committee' and the Chiefs of Staffs Sub-Committee on Biological Warfare. The Medical Research Council paid the salaries of the group and were reimbursed by the Ministry of Supply but otherwise played little real role in activities at Porton.

The group, which arrived at Porton in early October 1940, was called the Biology Department, Porton (BDP). The exact method whereby Fildes was selected is now obscure: it is certain that he had been consulted in earlier years. In 1959 he wrote that 'I was invited by the MRC to undertake experiments on BW at Porton'. His obituary almost gives the impression that he appeared before the earlier CID Sub-Committee and offered his services. Fildes was one of the foremost microbiologists of the era. He was 58 in 1940, a formidable, stern, dictatorial and highly respected senior medical man who had been a naval surgeon in the Great War and who since 1934 had directed the Medical Research Council Unit in Bacterial Chemistry at the Middlesex Hospitals' Bland Sutton Institute of Pathology. He was the third of the seven children of Sir Luke Fildes RA, a prominent Victorian artist who eventually became a fashionable and royal portrait painter. A rich man and a life-long batchelor, he lived through most of his stay at Porton at the onetime Old George Hotel in Salisbury's High Street. Fildes and his group arrived at Porton surrounded by great secrecy, great import and the greatest priority, all of which tended to engender some local resentment. Fildes enjoyed brushes with authority and lost no time in publicising to Hankey any inadequacies encountered at Porton in his strenuous attempts to set up the group. Attempts by the Commandant and Chief Superintendent to integrate BDP more closely under CDES command and management failed. Bureaucracy was anathema to Fildes and he insisted that communication between himself and Hankey, and later Duff Cooper, was direct and exclusive. He also made it quite clear that decisions on the research programme were to be made by him and not by the biological warfare Sub-Committee. Again, in 1959 he wrote 'The Chiefs of Staff did not direct the work. In fact, no one directed it except the scientists involved; the Chancellor of the Duchy of Lancaster was "responsible".' It is important to realise that BDP was, even with the exigencies of war which must have evoked many unconventional groups, a highly individualistic

body. This characteristic continued well after the end of the Second World War and to a degree its successors were always atypical Ministry Establishments.

Initially BDP consisted of less than a dozen medical men, scientists and technicians, most of whom had been brought by Fildes from his Medical Research Council unit. Others including Dr D W W Henderson, soon to emerge as Fildes' deputy, came at the instigation of Sir John Ledingham, from the Lister Institute. The staff eventually grew by the attachment of three or four scientists from CDES, the arrival of a few RAMC officers and men, the local recruitment of junior staff and the eventual attachment of several American bacteriologists commissioned as US Army and Navy Officers. The total BDP staff probably never exceeded some 50 people of diverse origins and backgrounds, including a peer of the realm, a gamekeeper and, a member of the Forte hotel and catering family called-up into the Royal Army Medical Corps. The group was housed initially in a small complex designed as an animal house for the Physiology Section of CDES. Soon this was extended and linked to new hutted laboratories. The ground floor of the main BDP building then largely reverted to offices and workshops, leaving the upper floor as laboratories. Above this a machine gun post for anti-aircraft defence was erected.

Fildes set out in his first report, before any experimental work had started, the ways in which he believed that microorganisms

The senior staff of the Biology Department at Porton in October 1943. Rear rank, from the left, Dr D Herbert, Dr G M Hills (in Home Guard uniform), Lieutenant J M Barnes RAMC, Lieutenant J M Ledingham RAMC, Dr D D Woods, Lieutenant (jg) USN MC, C Howe, Ensign H N Carlisle USN MC, and Lieutenant C E Venzke USA VC. Those seated, from the left, Dr G P Gladstone, Lieutenant W B Sarles USN MC, Dr D W W Henderson, Dr Paul Fildes, Dr J F S Stone, Lieutenant Colonel A Nimmo Smith RAMC and Lord Stamp.

might be used in war. Some such ways were identified as lesser possibilities for a variety of reasons. It was decided to concentrate on microorganisms disseminated as an aerosol from bursting munitions or from sprays, and to examine the effects of inhalation of the aerosol, the respiratory tract being eminently vulnerable to invading microorganisms. Unlike the situation with chemical agents such as mustard gas, the undamaged skin was relatively proof against microorganisms. Most chemical agents exerted their effects as gases, vapour or liquids. With biological agents, there were no gases or vapours; aerosol particles small enough to be carried through the air and thence deep into the lungs were produced from bursting munitions or from sprays. Firstly, methods had to be devised and evaluated in the laboratory and then in the field. Further, the infectious diseases that were of greatest significance had to be determined. The design of bombs and sprays for dissemination leant heavily on CDES, which had nearly 25 years of experience in gas weapons. CDES also provided much expertise and facilities for field trials and in adapting laboratory production of microorganisms to semi-technical scales to provide enough suspension of bacteria for experimental bomb filling and trials.

By 1942 BDP had shown that several species of laboratory animal could be fatally infected by the inhalation of a defined quantity of spores of the bacterium Bacillus anthracis, the causative agent of anthrax. They had shown (using a harmless naturally occurring sporing bacterium isolated from hay on the Porton Range) that sufficient quantities of spores could be produced in the optimum range of aerosol particle size from bomblets and that a simulant agent cloud could regularly and reproducibly pass downwind from the bomblets at significant concentrations such that if the simulant were to be replaced by anthrax spores, then infection and death were sure to follow in animals and presumably in men exposed to the aerosol. Anthrax spores could not be safely released from bomblets or sprays on the Porton range but it was essential to show that munitions charged with anthrax spores would behave as expected and produce casualties under realistic conditions. Accordingly, the remote Gruinard Island (at the time known for security reasons as 'X-Base') off the coast of Ross and Cromarty in Scotland was requisitioned as an isolated and safe site for trials and in 1942 and 1943 a team from BDP, assisted by CDES and Service staff conducted bomblet trials on the island. The story of these trials, kept secret for many years, has now become well known. The contamination of a small part of the island, the subsequent purchase of the island by Ministry of Defence until such time as the island was safe for man or beast and the eventual decontamination of the contaminated site using formaldehyde in sea water in the late 1980s after CDE had taken the initiative to solve the problem once and for all, lead to the return of the island to civil use in 1990.

The Gruinard Island trials and a further single trial at a Penclawdd beach on the Gower coast (which left no contamination because the site was subsequently washed by the tide) confirmed that sheep could be fatally infected under realistic conditions. It was deduced that deaths in personnel were certain to follow an exposure 200 yards downwind of the explosion of such a munition and that a serious risk extended for more than twice that distance. Further, on a weight-to-weight basis, the particular agent was 100–1000 times more potent than any then known chemical agent.

The United Kingdom made its data available to the US and Canada in pursuit of an Allied programme for a retaliatory biological capability in what was later to be called the 'N[1]-bomb' project based on 500 lb cluster bombs containing over 100 small 4 lb bomblet sub-munitions of the type which had been trialled latterly on Gruinard Island. Such clusters had been shown by the use of simulants in trials at Porton to produce an effective aerosol concentration of spores over nearly 100 acres from a small impact area. The United Kingdom had no large scale biological agent production plant and no facilities for field trials with cluster bombs charged with the actual agent. Plans were made to produce anthrax spores in America and to trial charged cluster bombs in Canada. In the event, fulfilment of the Allied plans was halted by the end of the war, before the plant erected by America had produced any anthrax spores.

The immediate War Cabinet requirement for the United Kingdom to have the means to retaliate-in-kind had however been fulfilled by 1943, by a weapon directed at livestock. BDP had determined that pending realisation of Allied plans for the anthrax cluster bomb, the only practical solution was a weapon requiring no special munitions or associated hardware, based on the charging of cattle-cake with anthrax spores and their subsequent delivery from the flare-chutes of bombers over the cattle-grazing pastures of Germany. The cakes would be readily found and eaten by cattle; each contained a lethal ingestion dose of spores.

It was envisaged that retaliatory use of the stockpile of 5,000,000 cattle-cakes in 'Operation Vegetarian' would strike a blow at Germany's already weak agricultural sector and, more importantly, underline the principle of retaliation-in-kind. The

---

1   N was the BDP and later Allied code for anthrax.

Cattle-cake charged with anthrax spores.
The stockpile of five million cakes was stored in cardboard boxes, each holding four hundred cakes. The boxes were sealed with adhesive tape, with a metal ring to facilitate operational opening.

concept had been devised and trialled using harmless cattle-cake on the Porton Ranges and the numbers of cakes needed for aircraft flying at various heights and speeds to cover specific areas with the optimum concentration of cakes had been determined. The charged cakes were produced in a small building known collo-quially, for reasons which are now obscure, as 'Foyles factory' and built in 1941 for the ad hoc small scale production of various chemical and smoke munitions. Since the cattle-cake were also known as 'buns'; the building soon became the 'Bun factory'. The empty cakes were made by a well-known soap maker of Old Bond Street and supplied to Porton on a 250,000 a week basis: their manufacture from ground linseed meal being based on a modified soap tabletting process. Equally well known sweet makers and biscuit makers had been apparently unable to undertake the task. No great curiosity seems to have been evinced by the order for cattle-cake. Porton designed charging and sealing machines which could inoculate 12,800 cakes a day. The cakes were then dried and packed in boxes of 400. Production began 15 weeks before Christmas 1942 and the stockpile was completed by 22 April 1943. This capability, once the process was established, was essentially run by one technician from BDP, 15 ladies from a Bristol soap factory who were employed at Porton during the war for ad hoc small production jobs, one laboratory assistant, two labourers and 'one boy to assist'. Apart from one or two boxes of cakes which were retained as memorabilia until 1972, the stockpile was des-troyed very soon after the end of the Second World War. Whilst this particular weapon may not have been of outstanding military significance, it was as Fildes wrote in 1943 'developed as the quickest way in which we could make some retaliation at short notice'. Its political significance is considerable: it is unlikely that any weapon of similar potential could be brought to operational availability with such simplicity, minimal resources and cost in its development and production.

The apotheosis of research at BDP was to demonstrate the feasibility of biological warfare by all means short of actual use in war and to provide some way for the United Kingdom to retaliate-in-kind in the event of such use by the Axis powers. Besides these notable achievements BDP pioneered in several unique fields, notably the semi-technical scale of pathogen pro-duction, and in experimental airborne infection, thus providing some of the earliest United Kingdom effort in the then embryonic sciences of biotechnology and aerobiology. In the future, the successors to BDP were to become acknowledged leaders in such fields.

The Post-War Years to the 1960s

4

The Nerve Agent Era and Abandonment of Offensive Capabilities by the United Kingdom

In the years immediately following the war there was little of the uncertainty about the future that had been evident at Porton after the Great War. Whilst chemical warfare had not been used in the Second World War and atomic weapons appeared to have eclipsed all else, the nerve agents were undoubtedly a major factor in ensuring that chemical warfare retained at least some part in United Kingdom military doctrine. It is perhaps difficult to appreciate the impact of these agents. Few earlier agents were quite so insidious. The well trained British serviceman was familiar with the characteristic smells of mustard, lewisite, chlorine, phosgene, BBC and KSK (ethyl iodoacetate): few of the older agents were odourless. A few whiffs of most of these at low concentration before the gas mask was donned would do little harm. However, with the highly potent, odourless, colourless nerve agents, able to exert rapid effects through skin, eyes and respiratory tract, no such latitude was possible. Demonstration of the actual effects of nerve agents on man and personal experience of the effectiveness of protective measures could not be built in to service training, as they were with the older agents. Unprotected men could not be put through gas chambers or allowed to see that if

A reunion of Second World War Portonians on 6 September 1946. Many senior figures are to be seen here, including the late Sir Owen Wansbrough-Jones, A E Childs, Sir Charles Lovatt Evans, Sir Harold Hartley, Sir Fredrick Bain, Professor D D Woods, Professor J S Kennedy and Sir Paul Fildes.

nerve agents were decontaminated swiftly from their skin no effects were exerted. Unlike most of the older agents, the margin between mild effects at low doses and death at higher doses was small: nerve agents could not be used in troop training. The problems of defence were now of a new sort. Equally, development of a United Kingdom chemical warfare capability based on nerve agents brought other problems in future production by industry, weaponising, trialling and stockpiling. Military usage and the role of nerve agents in differing types of warfare had to be considered in detail.

At Porton, the Station now had a civilian Chief Superintendent, Mr A E Childs. (A civilian Chief Superintendent post was created in 1941 to parallel the Military Commandant. When the title of Commandant was dropped in 1942, the Chief Superintendent post became military). In February 1948, the directorship of Porton was vested for the first time in a civilian Chief Superintendent, a title which continued until 1956, when it was changed to Director. Childs, a physical chemist, had been at Porton since the early 1920s becoming successively Head of Chemistry Section in 1938, Deputy Superintendent of Experiments in 1940 and Superintendent for Research and Development from 1941–1942. In 1949 he returned to London as Director of the headquarters Directorate where he had spent much of the war as Principal Technical Advisor to the Director. He continued to serve on several official advisory bodies during the 1950s.

In 1948 there was the expected post-war departure from war work to the universities and industry. Staff numbers contracted from the over a 1000 complement of the war to about 800 in 1953. Superimposed on staff problems were the massive lack of modern facilities and the effects of the ravages of war-time shortages and lack of repairs and upkeep. However, in the subsequent era of post-war austerity and continued shortages, followed by defence cut after defence cut, the wonder is that the Establishment survived at all.

Despite the desperate preoccupation with the nerve agents, diverse new roles were being adopted and lodger units became a feature of life at Porton. Towards the end of the Second World War in 1944, responsibility for military use of DDT fell to the Chemical Defence Directorate and Porton; control of the malarial mosquito in the Far East and elsewhere had become a major problem for British and Imperial troops. Porton established an entomology section under Dr (later Professor) J S Kennedy FRS where work on locusts, mosquitos, flies, bed bugs, lice and all insects of military importance could be done. Full-scale field trials

Porton staff at the German chemical warfare station at Raubkammer bei Munster in 1945. Most, though temporarily uniformed, were civilians, who can be readily distinguished in this photograph by having no cap badges. The post-war exploitation of German chemical weapons at Raubkammer was particularly important. It was here that the British came across German 105 mm shells marked with three green rings, which on examination were found to contain remarkable potent and hitherto unknown organophosphorus nerve agent.

involving DDT spraying from aircraft over mosquito-ridden areas could not be undertaken by the Ministry of Production. Because of the expertise and facilities at Porton and the analogies between pesticide dissemination and chemical warfare Porton was eminently suited for such a role. This work was subsequently coordinated by the Colonial Insecticides Committee under Professor Sir Ian Heilbron. The Colonial Office Anti-Locust Research Centre, South African departments, the International Red Locust Control Service and Porton subsequently mounted trials in Tanganyika in which eight Anson aircraft sprayed the Porton formulation of the pesticide DNOC, with highly successful results. In 1948 the Colonial Office stationed its own research unit at Porton with the title Colonial Office Pesticide Research Unit. CDES still maintained its own small entomology section for a few years but the Colonial Office unit was maintained at Porton with many changes of title; the last being as an Overseas Development Natural Resources Institutes unit which left CDE's Closed Area for its new home at Chatham in April 1990.

In 1947 the Medical Research Council set up its new Toxicology Unit within the main Physiology Section at CDES under Dr J M Barnes, who had served as an RAMC officer in BDP during the Second World War and who, until his untimely death, was widely regarded as an outstanding toxicologist. The unit pioneered research in the toxicology of pesticides, beryllium, plasticisers and other industrial hazards but in 1950 moved to Carshalton where it still continues. The Medical Research Council (known as the Medical Research Committee until 1920) had been involved with chemical warfare matters since the Great War and

through its own Chemical Warfare Medical Committee had
published at least eighteen major reports and an 'Atlas of Gas
Poisoning'. The Medical Research Committee was represented on
the original Chemical Warfare Committee by notable men of
medicine and science such as Sir Henry Dale and J S Haldane. It
continued to be peripherally involved with matters of chemical
defence (and later biological defence) until some time in the 1950s.
Occasionally it instigated unusual ad hoc activity at Porton. In 1945
the Medical Research Council had been asked by the War Office
to investigate the possible hazard to personnel from operating
Radar. It was subsequently agreed that this would be done under
the aegis of the Medical Research Council at Porton, with
Professor J S Young of Aberdeen University Pathology Department and Professor G R Cameron of University College Hospital,
London providing the histological expertise. The work was classi-
fied Secret and given the deliberately obscure title of the 'High
Frequency Dehydration Project'. Accordingly rats were exposed in
different ways to the emanations from Radar equipment parked
outside the Physiology Section and run by a unit of the Royal
Electrical and Mechanical Engineers. The final report on the study
was presented to the Council in 1947 and demonstrated the
unlikelihood of Radar operators being affected in any way by
radiation. The tradition of both ad hoc studies in fields remote
from chemical defence and of lodger units continued. In 1991,
small units of the Defence Quality Assurance Directorate, Royal
Ordnance Plc and other organisations are sited within Porton.

The advent of the nerve agents had indirectly emphasised the
inadequacies of Porton's ageing facilities and the inappropriateness
of the layout of much of the camp. Porton had grown higgeldy-
piggeldy without much consideration of safety, logic or aesthetics.
The traditional Porton small, scattered, individual buildings increased fuel and maintenance costs and encouraged the isolation
of small autonomous groups. In 1947 Edgar Bateman who had
been at Porton since 1922, was Head of the Technical Chemistry
Section during the Second World War and then after a period in
London returned as Superintendent of the Field Services Division
and later became Deputy Chief Superintendent, prepared a plan
for the 'modernisation of toxicological warfare' embracing both
chemical and biological fields. What has since become known as
the Bateman Plan was intended to rebuild the facilities at Porton
and Sutton Oak over a number of years on a compact and orderly
basis and to enable the range at Porton to be used more effectively
for trials with highly toxic material. Housing and similar facilities
were also included. The plan was approved but inevitably defence

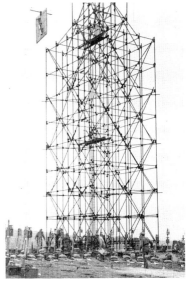

A trial to evaluate the hazard from chemical shell in the 1950s. The shell will be fired from the inverted mortar seen suspended from the tower. Below is the target of white card surrounded by a grid of sampling devices and an arc of more sophisticated samplers.

economies caused the postponement and then the indefinite shelving of the plan. The only parts which were implemented were modern engineering workshops, the siting of what was later to become the MRE on land adjacent to CDEE and the provision of Ministry of Supply housing estates in Salisbury. Aesthetics have played little part in the evolution of Porton, where economy and functionalism in architecture have predominated but in recent times many eyesores have been removed or tidied up. The programmes of tree and shrub planting which were started by the long defunct Ministry of Works, the Defence Land Agent and the Property Services Agency in recent times, have enhanced the surroundings considerably. The woods which stretch from the Idmiston Arch entrance to the old Mess and the avenues planted in the 1930s which line the principal roads within the older areas of the Establishment are now mature. Those avenues which were planted in the early 1950s to line the new road running from the then CDEE past the new MRD building have also now achieved a considerable effect. Porton has probably never looked better than in 1992.

A major but little known task was imposed on Porton in 1945. This was the writing of a series of reports on chemical warfare and chemical defence as a part of the Ministry of Supply Permanent Records of Research and Development during the Second World War. Some 86 monographs on chemical warfare topics were called for but many were never written or remain as drafts. At least 23 of those that were published are available in the Public Record Office. Surprisingly they are rarely referenced by authors.

As after the Great War, in the years after the Second World War, where the exigencies of the nerve agent programme permitted, the Establishment turned to remedy deficiencies in basic research, especially the theoretical and experimental investigation of the diffusion of particulates over long distances, the physics of aerosolisation of liquids and powders, absorbents, filter theory and a detailed study of the biochemistry of the nervous system.

As research on the nerve agents progressed, the Services and the Home Office, equipped with Porton's assessment of offensive potential and the hazard arising from use against British troops and the civil population, could now issue their formal requests for the types of nerve agent-based munitions and for the new protective measures they required. On the offensive side, GB, known to the Germans as Sarin, emerged as the particular nerve agent on which UK chemical weapons were to be based. A series of bombs for RAF use was required. The Army requirement centred around a 25 lb shell and a munition for the 4.2 inch mortar. Later in the 1950s when the V-series of nerve agents was discovered, there was Service interest in air and army weapon systems for the dissemination of the even more toxic VX, a low volatility, thick, oily liquid with remarkable percutaneous toxicity, considerable penetrative powers and the ability to persist on contaminated terrain or equipment for days or weeks. In the event, development work at Porton and at Nancekuke for the future United Kingdom chemical warfare capability in the decade after VJ day led to nothing because of the 1957 decision to abandon chemical weapons. Nevertheless, and most importantly, this post-Second World War excursion into the realms of offensive thinking and preparations, gave us an excellent understanding of how other nations could use similar chemical weapons against the United Kingdom and its forces.

On the defensive side, service requirements were stated for a real-time detector for nerve agent in the field, shipboard detectors for RN vessels, prophylaxis and therapy for nerve agent poisoning, a new Service respirator, collective protection for specific facilities, ships and vehicles, the means of monitoring decontamination and the residual contamination of terrain and equipment. The procurement cycle for some such items was relatively quick. For others the process was one of continuous improvement through several Marks reflecting advances in science and technology. In the 1950s–1960s the Establishment possessed a large self-contained engineering department heavily committed to development work and with highly specialised areas for rubber and polymer technology, textiles, and the design of plant and weapons. At one time, twelve engineers, fifteen drawing office staff and eighty mechanics staffed this then important and large part of the Establishment.

In 1949 Childs was succeeded as Chief Superintendent by a biologist, Dr H M Barrett, the Head of the Canadian Experimental Station at Suffield. This two year posting was in the nature of an exchange; Dr E A Perren of CDES being appointed to take Barrett's place at Suffield. It was largely at Barrett's instigation that twin 22 feet diameter test spheres were built at Porton, to provide containment in which to study agent aerosols produced by bursting munitions.

By late 1951 Barrett had been succeeded as Chief Superintendent by Mr S A Mumford, who had joined the Station in 1923 and became successively Head of Chemistry Section and Superintendent of the Research Division. Mumford had been engaged in his early years on the chemistry and physical chemistry of mustard gas. With the advent of the Second World War he became the leading authority on practical problems of detection, protection and decontamination and made notable contributions to anti-gas matters in the ARP Department. He was also largely responsible for the development of effective means of using the insecticide DDT in South-East Asia Command in the latter stages of the Second World War.

When Mumford retired in 1955 he was succeeded by Dr Perren, the post of Chief Superintendent being replaced by that of Director in 1956. Perren, who continued as Director until retirement in 1961, was essentially a research chemist of high calibre, who had come to Porton in 1922, became Head of Technical Chemistry Department in 1941, Superintendent of Development Division in 1947 and was the Head of Chemistry Section and Superintendent of the Research Division until 1955. When Perren retired as Director in 1961, he returned to the laboratory and spent several years studying a range of highly toxic chemical compounds. Perren is also remembered for his extensive activities in the post-war intelligence exploitation of the German chemical warfare capability.

Most areas of the Establishment have seen major changes since the end of the Second World War. Fundamental studies on aerosols which became the major role of the old Physics Section and later the Physics Division, have waxed and waned: there is now no such Division though aerosol is retained in the title of the present Detection and Aerosol Division. Smoke studies, once another major facet of life have disappeared. The supply of experimental animals, which during the war had been the responsibility of the Royal Army Veterinary Corps, was from 1949 catered for by the Animal Farm, which for some years from 1954 became known as Allington Farm, Porton and for rather more years was an autonomous Establishment with its own Superintendent and an intensive agricultural role in cereals, sheep and beef cattle. This later reverted to its parent Establishment. Its progress resembles that of the former outpost at Nancekuke in Cornwall which was once an autonomous Ministry of Supply facility from 1953–1962, when it became the Process Research Division of CDEE, then the Process Chemistry Division of CDE and eventually closed in 1979. Porton has never been immutable or rigidly fixed: it has always sought to move with the times. In fact, it appears to be in a constant flux, punctuated by brief periods of stability of role, complement, and aim. Inevitably, most flux has been occasioned by external political factors though there is a small tradition of internal reorganisation throughout Porton's 75 years, which on closer inspection seems generally to have served no real purpose.

To provide a succinct history of even the first 20 post-war years is difficult. Firstly, there is too much to summarise effectively. Secondly, there are topics which for reasons of national security, cannot be fully reported. Thirdly, there are many recent aspects which cannot yet be seen in their proper perspective. The first 20 years or so of the post-war period at Porton can be characterised by the change to civilian directorship, by the preoccupation with the nerve agents and on a national and policy basis by the abandonment of both the offensive research programmes and the production plants and weapons to retaliate-in-kind in the face of chemical attack in any future wars.

The Rise and Fall of Biological Warfare and Defence

In the aftermath of the war, as with CDES, there was a rapid exodus from BDP. Fildes, now knighted for his wartime services, and most of the senior staff returned to their institutes or university laboratories. D W W Henderson, who had been Fildes' right hand man remained. Ostensibly he was still a member of staff of the Lister Institute but with Fildes' backing he remained at Porton. In January 1946 with Henderson as Chief Superintendent, BDP became MRD, still co-located within CDES, still a well defined autonomous unit but continuing to rely on CDES for many services and collaborating with CDES on many aspects of research and development.

The success of the trials on Gruinard Island and research in subsequent years by the United Kingdom, the United States and Canada, had convinced the Chiefs of Staff and the Government that further study of biological warfare was essential. Though the

development of a United Kingdom nuclear weapon capability had a profound effect on military doctrine, biological warfare was still perceived to be of great significance and the need for the United Kingdom to possess a retaliatory capability had not diminished. The contemporary importance of biological warfare was reflected in the construction of a vast new £2.25 million building for MRD adjacent to the senior Establishment. Building began in 1948 and MRD moved to its new location in the summer of 1951. The construction of this new Establishment in a period of extreme austerity and pre-occupation with nuclear weapons emphasises the perceptions of the military utility of biological warfare which existed in earlier years. Early United Kingdom post-war policy and doctrine was still orientated around the eventual production of 1000 lb cluster bombs charged with anthrax for RAF use. No immediate Army or Navy requirement was apparent, though the distant prospect of rocket-type missiles with cluster warheads was noted. Several other agents had shown promise. The fundamental requirement was identified as detailed and long range study of the processes underlying biological warfare and defence: the ad hoc weapon studies necessary in the war had no place in the programme of fundamental research on the growth of bacteria, the behaviour and detection of bacterial aerosols, pathogenesis, microbial genetics and immunology.

Experimental biological weapon design devolved to CDES, which by 1948 had become CDEE. Staff recruitment for MRD was initially slow; microbiology was something of a new discipline and well qualified workers were scarce. Henderson's reaction was to recruit the most able scientists he could find, irrespective of their degree subjects and send them to his former colleagues and friends at the Post Graduate Medical School or the Lister Institute in London for appropriate training. Such unorthodoxies required support in high places since they involved much disruption of normal civil service practices. Henderson disliked bureaucrats and looked for high level support of a more independent nature. In

The newly-opened Microbiological Research Department at Porton in 1951.

1946 he wrote to Fildes telling of the intent that a high level advisory body be created and stating that he had 'complete assurance that there will be no stooge in the Ministry who will control or direct the work of my Department'. In 1946 the Ministry of Supply Advisory Council on Scientific Research and Technical Development (later the Ministry of Defence, Defence Scientific Advisory Council) set up a new constituent body, the Biology Research Advisory Board (always described colloquially as 'BRAB') under the chairmanship of Lord Hankey and with distinguished members such as Professor E C Dodds (the distinguished biochemist and physician, later Sir Charles Dodds), Sir Paul Fildes (now returned to the Medical Research Council), Sir Howard Florey (of penicillin fame, and later Lord Florey), Lord Stamp (one of the original BDP staff who had spent most of the war years on liaison duties in the US and Canada; by now Professor of Bacteriology at the Post Graduate Medical School) and O H Wansbrough-Jones (later Sir Owen) representing the senior and sister Chemical Defence Advisory Board. Departmental representatives included the Principal Director of Scientific Research (Defence) and Henderson. In time the BRAB grew bigger under the successive chairmanship of Lord Hankey and Sir Charles Dodds, only to wane under the chairmanship of Sir David Evans, and eventually disappeared before closure of MRE in 1979.

The move to the new building took place in the summer of 1951. Advance parties had gone ahead to set up MRD's miniscule administrative offices. The laboratories moved in phases, over a period of about a month, using now rarely seen RAF 'Queen Mary' long-load vehicles. The vacated buildings reverted to CDEE use, though after some years the hutted laboratories were demolished. 'Foyles factory', which had become the BDP and then MRD animal house, was eventually converted into laboratories.

One of the earliest MRD activities was to commission plans by CDRE at Sutton Oak and CDEE engineers on the design of a pilot-plant for studies on the means whereby bacteria might be produced on a large scale. This was eventually built in and around the hangar of a onetime Tank Armaments Research outpost on 'Gas Compound Road' leading to the now gone remains of 'Gas Wood'. None of the CDRE or CDEE engineers were familiar with microbiology but they were knowledgeable on plant for highly toxic material. Equally, none of the MRD staff involved initially knew much about microbiology. Most were industrial chemists, who were soon dispatched by Henderson for training elsewhere. Eventually the MRE pilot plant and its staff were recognised as world leaders, especially in the safety containment of microbial plant and

in the theory of continuous culture. The plant was taken over by CAMR, with the main MRE building in April 1979.

Despite the emphasis on broad-based and fundamental studies at MRD and MRE, there was considerable pressure from the Chiefs of Staff, through the Inter Services Sub-Committee on Biological Warfare to evaluate the behaviour of agents and munitions in the most realistic way through trials in the field, as had been done on Gruinard Island. Largely, MRD took the view that it was necessary to know the mechanisms underlying phenomena, rather than merely know of their existence; a necessity usually fulfilled by painstaking laboratory work, rather than against the traditional background of meteorological uncertainties and vast resources and personnel removed from the laboratory to distant locations for months on end. However in 1948 MRD with the support of the Chiefs of Staff, BRAB, CDEE and the Services, began Operation HARNESS, the first of five major trials which were carried out at sea. Gruinard Island was now seen as unsuitable on several counts, notably safety limitations caused by wind direction and the proximity of the mainland. Some search was made for an alternative island site in United Kingdom waters but in the end it was decided to explore the use of the sea as a range. Trials at sea would not be restricted for safety reasons by latitude and wind direction and there would be no contamination of terrain, pathogenic microorganisms would be diluted to extinction by the

Part of the Chemical Defence Experimental Establishment in the 1960s: much of the detritus of the war years has gone and the growth of trees has done much to enhance the appearance.

sea and the air, and also sunlight would be a factor in destroying infectivity. The essentials of such trials were the dissemination of agent aerosols from a bursting munition or spraying device carried on a float, situated up-wind of an array of air sampling devices and animals in an arc of rubber dinghies. The factors affecting particle fall-out, virulence and viability could be evaluated and compared with results obtained under laboratory conditions. In later trials the techniques became modified and sections of 'Mulberry harbours' were used as pontoons.

Operation HARNESS (1948–1949) took place in waters off the Bahamas 'to determine the practicability of conducting BW trials at sea'; using greater distances than on Gruinard Island with three bacterial agents. It confirmed the practicability of sea trials and the utility of certain bacteria other than anthrax as agents.

Operation CAULDRON (1952) was held in May–September off Stornaway in the Isles of Lewis with the aim of consolidating data gained in Operation HARNESS and to assess the utility of a further bacterium.

Operation HESPERUS (1953) was also done in Scottish waters to consolidate data and to compare the efficiency of several munitions and sprays.

Operation OZONE (1954) saw a return to a site 20 miles off Nassau to acquire more data on spraying agents and for the first time, on a virus.

Operation NEGATION (1954–1955), also off the Bahamas, compared the loss of viability in three aerosolised agents and a second virus.

The magnitude of these trials over nearly a decade, like the scale of the MRD building, serves to remind us of the status and priority once accorded to biological warfare research. The 4,000 ton tank landing ships HMS BEN LOMOND and HMS NARVIK, which had been re-fitted as floating laboratories for these trials, were eventually laid up and later broken up. Sea trials with pathogens on the same scale eventually became an impossibility, due both to diminishing resources and the lack of impetus due to abandonment of United Kingdom aims to develop a retaliatory capability.

After the removal from CDEE to the new MRD building, the inauguration of an influential BRAB, the success of the early sea trials and staff increases, MRD increased its international status, not only in the biological warfare community but as a centre of excellence in several areas of microbiology and allied disciplines. Its success was undoubtedly due to Henderson's driving force and his long held view that the two major pitfalls to be avoided were developing a rigid organisation and attacking a too wide range of problems. Whilst MRD work still had a very high priority, reflecting the Chiefs of Staff intent that biological warfare research should equate to that on atomic energy, Henderson still had to fight to obtain the resources that he deemed essential. Sir Owen Wansborough Jones (a former Chief Scientist of the Ministry of Supply) described Henderson as having 'an innate distrust and general contempt for authority and the establishment, which he did nothing to conceal ... but who always recognised his duty nationally and so long as he could continue exploring fundamentals, never overlooked his special and peculiar responsibility'. Lesser luminaries and MRD staff had great regard for this patriarchal figure, often tinged with some apprehension about his ready shows of displeasure.

By 1957 the infectious levels for at least 15 species of microorganisms had been determined and a great understanding of the factors affecting airborne travel of aerosol particles and of the mechanisms of inhalation infection had been achieved. Significant progress had been made on the chemical nature of virulence, continuous culture, aerobiology, immunochemistry and bacterial genetics and a start had been made on the newer discipline of virology. The indication from earlier sea trials that the strategic potentials of biological warfare were considerable and hitherto unappreciated, was of great significance. Subsequent trials by CDEE and MRE, using inert particles or harmless microorganisms as simulants, showed that the strategic deployment of biological warfare against the United Kingdom or United Kingdom forces posed an immense hazard and that a prime need existed for an early warning device for biological agents in the atmosphere. Other research showed the considerable potential for clandestine, unattributable sabotage and small scale attack by biological agents in a wide variety of situations.

In 1957 MRD became MRE and the title of Chief Superintendent was changed to Director, thus according the same status to both major Porton Establishments. 1957 saw other changes at Porton, notably the departure of the Royal Artillery battery and the take-over of the barracks by the local offices of the Ministry of

Public Buildings and Works. The period also brought a Cabinet Committee decision to abandon any aims to develop an offensive capability in biological warfare (and to destroy all existing chemical agent stocks and abandon the programme to produced a nerve agent based chemical warfare capability). Nancekuke began the run-down immediately but at MRE, where the accent had always been on research, rather than development, no specifically offensive research was underway. Very few MRE staff had been involved with offensive matters since the Second World War, and as far as MRE research was concerned, the Cabinet Committee decision had no immediate effect. Nevertheless, it was to be of profound importance in the future.

The Last Three Decades
1960–1990

5

Whilst this period is characterised by the solely defensive role adopted by the United Kingdom, it is paradoxically a period of mounting concern about the chemical threat, about actual or suspected use of chemical warfare in several nations, about almost explosive proliferation of chemical and biological warfare capabilities in many areas of the world, and the increasing offensive potentials arising from developments in science and technology. These concerns were concurrent with increased momentum for chemical weapons arms control, with the Biological Weapons Convention of 1972 linked (again paradoxically) with a subsequent increased perception of biological threats, an enhancement of the biological hazard (through recombinant-DNA technology and biotechnology) and with the United Kingdom focus for biological defence at Porton devolving from MRE to CDE. The complexities of describing the last three decades are considerable. The Kent history finished in the late 1950s and there is no single source of summarised later activity at Porton that can be used.

Into the Ministry of Defence 1960–1970

In 1959 the Ministry of Supply was disbanded and CDEE, together with MRE, Allington Farm and Nancekuke passed to the War Department. By 1961 the Establishment at Nancekuke had become the Process Research Division of CDEE. Parts of the peripheral east and south-east areas of the range were let, for the first time, to local farmers. Building continued and by 1965 the Establishment possessed new chemistry and physics buildings. In 1964 CDEE and MRE passed into the newly constituted Ministry of Defence. The 1960s were marked also by high level studies on chemical and biological defence needs under the Chairmanship of Sir Alexander Todd (later Lord Todd), by the American military use of the riot-control agent CS in Vietnam, the reputed use of chemical warfare by Egypt against Royalist factions in the Yemen and by the use of CS in Northern Ireland by the police and the army. On the arms control front and in the political arenas of several nations, matters connected with chemical and biological warfare were attracting increasing attention and continued to do so throughout the 1960s and 1970s. Arms control aims, high level consideration of chemical and biological defence policy, the use of CS for internal security and allegations of chemical warfare were all eventually in various ways, to exert effects on activities and events at Porton.

Despite the abandonment of aims for an offensive capability and the exclusive commitment to defensive research at Porton, suspicion and opprobrium continued in Parliamentary and public circles. This was however of little concern to most at Porton. The tradition of heaping abuse on Porton and Portonians was after all well established; the press was an ever-ready means. Magazines such as the now defunct 'John Bull' and 'Titbits' seemed to have been particularly fascinated by Porton in the 1920s and 1930s eg 'Our Poison Gas Men: the Truth' in 'John Bull' of 7 October 1933. Recruitment was undoubtedly affected by opprobrium and Ministers were rather more sensitive than Portonians. To some extent successive post-war Governments had contributed to un-ease and suspicions. Secrecy had always attended decisions on matters of chemical and biological defence and the decision unilaterally to abandon retaliatory programmes was made in secret. The 'protective measures only' policy was not made evident for some years and even then was not clearly stated. Probably the first definitive Ministerial statements were made in 1968 and 1969 when open weeks were held at MRE and then CDEE (and at Nancekuke in 1970) to clarify roles and to demonstrate that the United Kingdom policy was solely one of defence, and that no secret facility for production of chemical or biological weapons existed or was envisaged. Thereafter the level of abuse diminished, demonstrations at the Porton establishments fell off considerably as the Committee of 100 and other factions lessened their interest in Porton.

Accidents and fatalities had always exacerbated public unease and Ministerial anxieties. The death of an RAF volunteer during nerve agent experiments at CDEE in 1953 and the 1962 death of an MRE scientist from an accidental plague infection had con-siderable repercussions at both Establishments in terms of im-proved and tightened, ethical, medical and safety requirements. Local authorities were often prompted by individuals or factions to undue concern about the possible effects on adjacent villages of release of chemicals or microorganisms if there was to be an air crash on the Porton campus. Anti-vivisectionists were another faction who had targeted Porton since at least the early 1920s. All these manifestations of unease about Porton combined almost insidiously to evoke changes over the years.

The Establishment also became increasingly involved in trauma studies. It had engaged sporadically in such work since at least 1937 and later continually in the context of the fulfilment of internationally agreed obligations to limit the injury potential of small arms bullets. The Colt Armalite rifle had been used against British forces in Malaysia, producing wounds worse than formerly encountered: the Establishment subsequently studied its effects. Later still, the Establishment was tasked to the need to establish and limit the injury potential of a range of weapons and devices, notably the baton round systems. All these activities involved close contact with other Establishments and the Services Medical Departments. Body armour, biochemical aspects of trauma and surgical problems were also studied at Porton and continued on matters arising from the Falkland's campaign and more recently from the Gulf hostilities, where the prospect of chemical agent-contaminated or infected wounds posed not only an increased hazard to the victim but a risk to medical and surgical teams.

In the mid-1960s, there were reports that Egyptian forces had used chemical weapons against royalist factions in Northern Yemen. Assessment of information on lethal and other effects and analysis of reputed residual chemical agent at Porton proved (like the United Nations investigations) somewhat inconclusive; those few samples reaching the United Kingdom showed only residues of tear gas. Nevertheless, it was clear that some more potent lethal agent must have been used and that establishing the validity of reputed chemical warfare in far-off places, let alone identifying the agent involved, was no simple process. In 1965, United States forces in Vietnam started to use the harrassing sternutator DM and the tear gases CN and CS against Viet Cong troops (The United States declared that their use was not contrary to the 1925 Geneva Protocol. Further, the United States had not then ratified the Protocol and was not bound by it). This use, and the use of defoliants in Vietnam, contributed to the increasing world wide concern about chemical and biological warfare.

Mr E E Haddon became Director of CDEE in 1961. He had been at the Chemical Defence Research Department HQ in London since 1929 and by 1943 headed its CDR1 branch which dealt with the development of antigas equipment. Later he became Personal Assistant to the Controller of Chemical Defence Development (Mr J Davidson Pratt). By 1952 Haddon was Assistant Director of Chemical Defensive Research and Development and by 1957, when Childs retired, he had become Director of the London HQ. Much of the post-war re-equipment of the Services for chemical defence arose from Haddon's efforts, both in London and later at Porton.

On 27 May 1966 the Establishment's 50th Anniversary was marked by a visit from the Duke of Edinburgh. This was the first visit of a member of the Royal family since that of King George V in 1918. Unlike the first visit, there are still documentary and film records of the 1966 royal progress at CDEE and MRE. With the Chief Scientist, Ministry of Defence (Army Department), the Deputy-Master General of the Ordnance, the Director of Biological and Chemical Defence, the Director of CDEE and the Director of MRE, the Duke met senior members of the scientific staff and the senior Service liaison officers, listened to presentations on research projects and saw the equipment under development for the Services. Much the same programme was repeated at MRE; some interesting detail has survived. At MRE the Duke of Edinburgh's car door was opened by Mr J L Smith, the Head Messenger and former NCO of the Royal Artillery, wearing Ministry messengers uniform, peaked cap, white gloves and medals. Some informative facts on the protocol for use of Royal Standards and the Union Jack in the context of flag poles fixed to buildings and free-standing flag poles have also been preserved. (The 60th Anniversary of CDE in 1976 seems to have attracted little attention, possibly because defence economies had called into question the very future of both the Establishments at Porton. However, Defence Public Relations staff produced a brief historical account of CDE in the form of a Diamond Jubilee folder which was used to jacket the Establishment brochure or any other printed ephemera of the period).

1966 also saw the 'Mercury' computer installed and the old gas retort house converted into a laboratory. (The Establishment had for long had its own gas works, producing the distinctively smelling Mansfield gas from oil. Somewhen in the early 1960s, 'town gas' reached Porton). 1968 brought an exacerbation of the international unease, when an aircraft spray trial at Dugway Proving Ground in the United States went awry and the nerve agent VX was disseminated off-target, resulting in the death of many hundreds of grazing sheep and the eventual need to destroy the whole flock of 6,000. An accident with VX also occurred at an American base in Okinawa, resulting in the hospitalisation of 23 US troops. Such incidents together with the American use of chemical agents in Vietnam increased the domestic and international opposition to United States chemical and biological warfare research and weapons programmes.

On the retirement of Haddon as Director in 1968, Mr G N Gadsby was appointed to the CDEE Directorship. A onetime

Riot Control

The value of 'gas' for riot control or police work had been apparent in America and several continental nations for nearly half a century. In the United Kingdom, there was little interest, although in the colonial police services of the Empire military tear gases had been available and occasionally used, for many years. No such use occurred in the United Kingdom until that of CS in August 1969. This resulted in concerns which led eventually to the Himsworth enquiry on the medical and toxicological aspects of CS. Sir Harold Himsworth initiated years of studies at Porton, leading to many official reports and several dozen open publications in the scientific literature by Porton staff. The Himsworth reports of 1969 and 1971 in effect vindicated MOD's earlier selection of CS as a more effective and safer replacement for the old tear gases such as choracetophenone (CAP or CN). CS was first synthesised in America in 1928 but it was not investigated at Porton until 1934 when it was screened as one of many possible military lachrymators or tear gases. CAP had also been used for years in many nations in military training, as a useful simulant for unpleasant or lethal war gases eg in respirator testing. However, it was not ideal for riot control and in the mid 1950s a search for something better began. Attention at Porton turned to some of the tear gases screened in the 1930s and CS was, after several years, accepted as a military replacement for CAP in 1958 and production studies begun at Nancekuke. The production of CS as both a military training aid and riot control agent for police use was transferred to civil industry in the late 1980s.

chemist, he was commissioned into the Royal Warwickshire
Regiment and later posted to the Royal Military College of Science
at Shrivenham, where he continued to lecture as a civil servant.
After posts at the then Army Operational Research Establishment,
he became its Director. Later, he was appointed to be Director of
Biological and Chemical Defence (by then the much diminished
London headquarters for the Porton Establishments and Nancekuke). At the time of his appointment to Porton, he was Deputy
Chief Scientist (Army) in the Ministry of Defence. Gadsby's
Directorship was marked by much international concern about
chemical and biological warfare, national concern about the riot
control agent CS and notably, in 1969, a week of open days at
CDEE. The Porton profile was substantially raised during this
period. Mr Gadsby's directorship was notable for the enhancement
of assessment and operational analysis work, which took place at
his instigation. Mr Gadsby was appointed to a senior post in the
British Defence Staff in Washington in 1972.

By 1969 President Nixon had been moved to abandon the
United States biological weapons capability, review policies on the
chemical weapons capability and announce his intention to sign the
coming Biological Weapons Convention and to submit the 1925
Geneva Protocol to the Senate for ratification: the United States
eventually ratified the Protocol in 1975. The Nixon renunciation
announcement on 25 November gave the reasons for the decision
to abandon the United States capability as the 'massive, unpredict-
able and potentially uncontrollable consequences' associated with
biological warfare. However, this abbreviated rationale was not
reflecting a view previously extant in the United States throughout
the quarter of a century of offensively related policies and research.
In recent years, after a decent interval, scholars are beginning to
say that the decision was essentially political, to draw attention
away from the longer established and proven chemical capability
recently used in Vietnam, to placate congressional, national and
international concern, and to enable the United States to make
progress in arms control. Domestic political considerations were
the main motivation and British proposals to separate chemical
from biological warfare in arms control efforts provided an opportunity for discarding unilaterally a whole method of warfare with
maximum publicity and minimal penalties. Regrettably, the Nixon
rationale has been reiterated over the years since 1969, as if the
United States had suddenly become aware of some hitherto
unperceived feature of biological warfare of sufficient magnitude to
render it militarily useless. This false rationale has bedevilled
biological defence efforts ever since. The conjoint effect of the

1969 Nixon renunciation and the advent of the 1972 Convention was synergistic. As biological warfare became unmentionable, it tended as a threat to become invisible. This dangerous lack of perception was almost fatal for biological defence research progress in several nations.

In its last two decades the MRE had two well defined roles: to assess the hazard of biological warfare and to devise the means of protection of the Armed Forces. This was, for many of the staff, a matter of fundamental research, where the link between topic and the role of the Establishment was tenuous. For others, it was more obvious and direct. MRE attracted many leading scientists whose interest in defence matters was limited: they were drawn to MRE by its reputation and its superb facilities. The accolade of acceptability had been given by much open publication of MRE work and by the presence of eminent figures on BRAB. Gradually, the majority of MRE scientists became engaged on work which was not in reality directly aimed at biological defence. As the inevitable and regular defence economies impinged, the integrity of multi-disciplinary teams at MRE could only be assured by undertaking work beyond the defence role. Budget cuts could be off-set by money from the civil sector. When Henderson retired in 1964, the situation appeared to be stabilising. It was accepted that the interests of the Establishment should widen. The facilities and expertise were without parallel and the similarity of many problems, whether they arose from some future use of biological warfare or whether from naturally occurring disease, led to work on behalf of the Ministry of Health, the Medical Research Council, the Public Health Laboratory Service and industry. The new Director Dr C E Gordon Smith brought further esteem to the Establishment by establishing it as a centre for arbovirus research and the investigation of urgent international public health problems such as the pathogenesis, identification and therapy of dangerous new infections such as Vervet Monkey Disease, Ebola Fever and Lassa Fever, and in the production of a wide variety of microbial products. Such work also gave MRE the opportunity to enhance its world leading status in microbial safety practices.

In 1968 a series of open days at MRE served largely to dispel some of the lingering suspicions that the United Kingdom policy was not confined to solely defensive work. Openness had always been a feature of the Establishment. In contrast to the necessary constraints placed upon CDE, most MRE work was unclassified and results were published openly in the scientific journals. Certain results of the wartime work by BDP had been published openly just after the war. By the mid-1970s 90% of the work was being published and by that time over 2500 scientific papers or lectures had been written or delivered by MRE staff.

More Economies and Uncertainties and the Demise of the Microbiological Research Establishment: 1970–1979

In 1970 the word 'Experimental' was dropped from the Establishment title, which was then to remain as CDE for the next 21 years and thus constitute something of a record, given the avidity with which titles had changed over the decades. The reason for the 1970 decision is now quite obscure. In the same year the Technical Information and Records Section was rehoused in a onetime laboratory and workshop block and a well-equipped lecture theatre arose within the shell of its earlier building. A large and modern animal house for the Medical and Biology Divisions was also erected on the site of the now demolished hutted laboratories which had been used for biological warfare research by BDP during the Second World War and later, until 1951, by its post-war successor the MRD. By 1971 changes were afoot in Whitehall: CDE now became an Establishment within the Procurement Executive of the Ministry of Defence. CDE's depleted headquarters, now in the Adelphi and the successor to the 1951 Chemical Defence Research Department, which latterly had been the Directorate of Biological and Chemical Defence (DBCD), became the Directorate of Research, Chemical and Biological (DRCB). It was under this title that it continued until its demise in the mid-1970s, when the tradition of a London headquarters which had been extant since the Great War, came to an end.

In 1972 Mr Gadsby was suceeded as Director by Mr T F Watkins, who had joined the then CDES in 1936. In 1939 he was seconded to the Chemical Defence Research Establishment in India and later headed the Research Divisions at Sutton Oak and Nancekuke. From 1956 he had been Head of Chemistry Section at the Establishment. In 1973 Allington Farm became a CDE Division; in later years the farming and laboratory animal breeding sides were separated into smaller units. A year later the Establishment's new ballistics facility for trauma studies was commissioned and on 1 July 1975, Lord Zuckerman, a former Chief Scientific Adviser to the Ministry of Defence, who was one of the pioneers in this field, notably on blast injury, made a formal visit to hear presentations and inspect the equipment in the facility. The Establishment's standing in this particular field of military medicine was now considerable and valuable contributions were (and still are) made to the surgical treatment of British casualties in

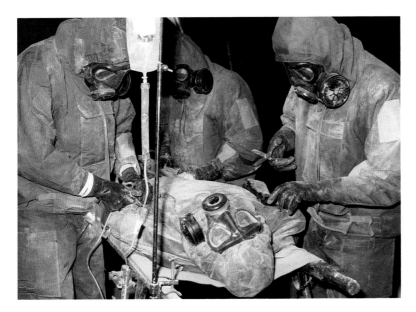

A tented chemical decontamination centre during a demonstration by a Field Ambulance and a Field Hospital of the RAMC.
This is an important stage in the evacuation of battlefield casualties, between the Regimental Aid Post and the Field Hospital. Here RAMC personnel are removing the casualty's NBC suit after its decontamination with fullers earth.

Northern Ireland, the Falklands war and elsewhere. By 1976 a review of the future of chemical and biological defence at the two Porton Establishments was again under way; economies were once again being sought and uncertainty prevailed. The United States ratification of the 1925 Geneva Protocol, the abandonment of the United States biological warfare capability, the coming into force of the 1972 Biological Weapons Convention, the threat from the Warsaw Pact and above all the need to slim programmes, reduce resources and save money, were all factors which affected the review. One consequence of the need for reduction in the defence budget was the seeking by CDE, and more so by MRE, of income from civil work: at one time the income at MRE from such work defrayed over 25% of the annual cost of the Establishment. The future of MRE had been a particular problem since the dissolution of the Ministry of Supply in 1957. The transfer to the War Department had been opposed by both the Director of MRE and the Biological Research Advisory Board of the Defence Scientific Advisory Council on the basis that the future welfare of the Establishment and its contribution to both biological defence and general microbiology could only be secured under civil control as a major national scientific asset, with the assurance of stable, long term control unaffected by the fluctuations of defence policy and spending and without the 'Service' label which was identified as deterring recruitment of the best staff. This view, presented to the War Department in 1960 did not prevail but was considered by the Todd Panel in its major review and later by an interdepartmental working party and at the highest levels in other departments. By 1970 the Ministry of Defence had agreed to continue biological defence research at MRE at the same level for at least a period of five years, before reappraising the situation in the light of events.

However, by the mid-1970s, most grave considerations on the very future existence of MRE were afoot. Dr Gordon Smith had been succeeded in 1971 by Dr R J C Harris, who was unwittingly to preside over the slow demise of the Establishment. The factors contributing to the decision to reduce the level of effort on biological defence and to close MRE are numerous, complex and interactive: they have been touched on earlier in this publication. In some ways MRE had subscribed to its own closure by venturing into non-defence research. It had been encouraged to do so by BRAB, the venture had massive public relations bonuses and it had achieved the stated aim of retaining unique multi-disciplinary teams within the Establishment. At the same time, this had evoked a fall-away of awareness on matters of biological warfare in other areas, an official realisation that a large Ministry of Defence Establishment was less than fully committed to Service requirements and even much official debate of the need for any United Kingdom effort on biological defence. All these factors interacted synergistically.

The 1970s were consequently a period of increasing unease at MRE. By the mid-1970s it had been decided that a reduced programme of biological defence research was acceptable and that this would be done by the transfer of a small team from MRE to CDE. The Central Policy Review Staff were invited to conduct a study on the possible future civil use of the staff and facilities of MRE, to ensure the perpetuation of a national centre of excellence in microbiology. The Medical Research Council was then asked to lead in a detailed review of the capability of MRE for civil research. Ultimately, the announcement was made that on 1 April 1979 the staff and facilities of MRE would be transferred to the Public Health Laboratory Service and become the Centre for Applied Microbiology and Research. The transfer of a small focus of expertise to continue biological defence studies would be enabled by the concurrent creation of a Defence Microbiology Division (DMD) within CDE.

For CDE, the possibility of being extinguished was more remote. Although chemical agents had played no part in a European war since 1918 and had not been used in the Second World War, they were perceived to pose not only a hazard but a specific threat to NATO. To continue chemical defence at some level was desirable, despite the need for concentrating resources in

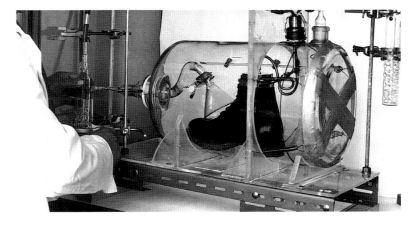

Measuring the penetration of a chemical warfare agent through an army boot.
Protection of the feet is especially important as the hazard from contaminated ground may, with certain agents, persist for many days after an attack.

support of the 'teeth' of the forces. This wisdom was later endorsed, as further aspects of not only the chemical threat from the Warsaw Pact emerged but of chemical capabilities in several potentially hostile and other nations. Notwithstanding, by 1974 a defence review of exceptional ferocity was in hand and by 1976, the decision had been taken to cut the budget for the Porton establishments, to close the CDE Process Research Division at Nancekuke and ultimately to close MRE and transfer responsibility for a much diminished biological defence role to CDE.

In May 1974 Mr Watkins retired as Director of CDE and was succeeded by Dr R G H Watson who had earlier been Director of Naval Research and Development Administration and from 1969 Director of the Admiralty Materials Laboratory at Holton Heath. On 30 September 1979 Nancekuke closed. The Officers' Mess, which had existed at several sites at Porton since 1916 closed at the same time as MRE. In 1979, a large new extension of the CDE chemistry facilities was started.

Biological Defence 1979–1991

The role of Defence Microbiology Division (DMD) was initially to maintain a focus of knowledge, advice and expertise relevant to biological defence within the Ministry of Defence and to act as a watchtower for significant developments in microbiology and other relevant sciences which might lead to a change in the threat. CDE had no special facilities for microbiological work, especially that involving the use of pathogens. Inevitably, for the new DMD, housed in part of a building designed for physics research, the settling-in process was slow and frustrating. The DMD role was almost immediately expanded to include CDE's newly acquired responsibility for Gruinard Island.

Gruinard Island

The problem of Gruinard Island had remained unsolved for decades. The owner had sought the return of the island in 1945 but the Ministry of Supply refused de-requisition on the grounds that the island was still contaminated as a result of wartime experiments and could not be returned until it was deemed safe. At that time due to great sensitivities about such matters the nature of the continuing contamination was never officially stated: when it inevitably became known, the opprobrium increased considerably. To allay the owners continuing concern the Crown had agreed in 1946 to purchase the island: when the contamination no longer existed the owner or her heirs would be able to re-purchase the island for the sale price of £500. Accordingly, the island was inspected yearly from 1947 to 1968 by a party from MRE and samples of terrain collected for the assay of the anthrax spores. No progressive diminution of the spores was found. Ways of removing or sterilising the island's top-soil had been studied in the 1970s but these were immensely costly or environmentally unacceptable. In 1978, in anticipation of CDE taking over responsibility a small joint CDE and MRE team made a survey. This was followed by a series of detailed visits and studies from 1979 to 1985 which re-addressed the question of the extent of the contamination and how decontamination of the terrain could be achieved. The contamination was found not to be widespread as had previously been assumed, but virtually limited to the immediate area of the wartime munition deployment, some three acres out of the 550 acre island. The prospects for decontamination were now much more encouraging. Improved techniques for the quantitative determination of anthrax spores were developed. Experiments were done to find the most practicable and efficient sporicidal chemical. A solution of formaldehyde in sea water eventually emerged as the disinfectant of choice. The Institute of Terrestial Ecology advised on the ecological acceptability.

The importance of the matter and the years of public debate and unease suggested that an independent body should maintain an overview of CDE's studies and plans. Accordingly the Independent Advisory Group on Gruinard Island was set up under the Chairmanship of Professor W D P Stewart FRS (then Boyd Baxter Professor of Biology at the University of Dundee, subsequently Secretary of the Agriculture and Food Research Council and now in 1992 the Chief Scientific Adviser at the Cabinet Office); an appointment made by the President of the Royal Society. CDE's conclusions on the efficacy of disinfection through irrigation of the contaminated area with a solution of formaldehyde in sea water and the identification of an appropriate contractor were endorsed. In June to August 1986, the decontamination was carried out. Tests to determine the efficacy of the decontamination were made in October 1986; these showed a few isolated residues of anthrax spores and re-treatment was done in July 1987. Further tests in October 1987 showed that all onetime positive sites were now yielding negative results. The indigenous rabbit population was examined for antibodies to anthrax; none were found. To demonstrate confidence in the decontamination procedure a flock of sheep was grazed on the island from May to October 1987, visited daily by a shepherd and his dog, and monthly by

Gruinard Island in 1986, as seen from the mainland.
The spit of shingle seen extending from right of the island provided a convenient landing place from the mainland jetty, both for the field trials teams of 1942 and 1943, and those from Porton and contractors who decontaminated sites on the island in 1986 in preparation for its 1990 return to civil ownership, nearly 50 years after its acquisition to meet urgent war time needs.

the District Veterinary Officer. There were no ill effects. Re-seeding of the treated areas resulted in a luxurious growth of grass. Taking all the facts into consideration the independent advisors concluded that 'the chances of persons or animals contracting anthrax on Gruinard Island are so remote that the island can be returned to civil use'. At a ceremony on the island on 24 April 1990 the Under Secretary of State for Defence announced that as the island was now 'fit for habitation by man and beast', the Ministry of Defence would return the island to the heirs of the previous owner on 1 May 1990. Nearly 50 years after the island was used to meet the desperate exigencies of war and 11 years after the custody of the island passed to CDE, the island was back in civil ownership.

The decontamination of Gruinard Island in 1986.
Contractor's personnel irrigating a contaminated area with a solution of formaldehyde in sea water: 50 litres were applied to every square metre of the ten acres so treated.

DMD continued meanwhile to formulate a biological defence research programme. Research had begun on rapid detection and identification methods for agents, on the anthrax bacillus, microbial toxins and on selected arboviruses. Work with certain pathogenic microorganisms initially involved the use of CAMR facilities, pending the adaptation or construction of new laboratories at suitable safety containment levels.

In the mid-1980s two matters combined to cause a further reappraisal of the level of biological defence effort. There were increased manifestations of the threat and the proliferation of biological warfare interest and activities in several nations was particularly alarming. The opportunities now provided by the development of recombinant-DNA technology (one of the aspects of the popular term 'genetic engineering') and massive developments in industrial microbiology for large scale production of microorganisms and microbial products were assessed as enabling a quantum leap in biological warfare. Further, a detailed look at the threat showed that these opportunities were now being explored elsewhere in the world. Subsequently, with the support of an independent advisory group (which though not directly subordinate to the Defence Scientific Advisory Council, as BRAB had been, was of similar status) the Ministry of Defence embarked on an enhancement of the biological defence programme at CDE, by building up a team of scientists within DMD to establish recombinant-DNA technology, identify priorities for its application in biological defence and assess how nations with a biological warfare capability might misuse the technology in improving their offensive programmes. The enhancement of DMD occurred during the 1980s and resulted in an increase in scientific staff. Developments in molecular biology and 'genetic engineering' are now being applied to assessments of biological hazards, rapid identification of agents and new vaccines. Biological defence is pursued energetically at CBDE, not only in DMD but in the Divisions concerned with detection of aerosols, with assessment and with field trials. As recorded elsewhere in this book, biological defence advice and equipment were prominent in the Establishment's support for Operation GRANBY in the Gulf War and those senior people of BDP once concerned with the first experimental study of the realities of this means of warfare at Porton during the Second World War would have been impressed with the speed and quality of the ad hoc support and advice provided from Porton.

The Establishment had provided support to the Foreign and Commonwealth Office for the successive Review Conferences of the 1972 Biological Weapons Convention since 1979. Original

Decontamination trials aboard ship 1981. Porton scientists probably first went to sea in 1923 when HMS "Princess Margaret" carrying 58 men from Porton sailed from Portsmouth for trials at Scapa Flow on the use of toxic smoke floats.

staff of DMD who came from MRE, latter day DMD staff and former MRE staff now in other areas of the Establishment have played a prominent part in detailed studies on developments in science which might affect the scope or the effectiveness of the Biological Weapons Convention and in analysis of States' Parties involvement in several Confidence-Building Measures, providing data on national activity and facilities of relevance.

Despite great vicissitudes over the years, support for arms control measures and research leading to the provision of effective protective equipment, drills and advice for the Services continues the tradition established in biological defence research over half a century ago, albeit that the option of retaliation-in-kind no longer forms part of the UK policy or programme. In 1991 plans were made for a new building within CBDE to house the major part of DMD's pathogen-handling laboratories and containment suites and so release the earlier adapted and ad hoc structures acquired in the early years of DMD for more suitable purposes. It is a little paradoxical that biological defence at Porton should have returned in 1979 to the 'Closed Area' of CBDE, where biological warfare research began nearly 40 years earlier and that MRE, once dedicated to such research, should have been absorbed by the Public Health Laboratory Service, a body originally founded for biological defence before the Second World War. MRE and its precursors had, from 1940–1979 only four civilian Directors. Most defence establishments changed Directors frequently: during the same period CDES and CDEE had been headed by 13 soldiers or civilians. Fildes died in 1971, Henderson in 1968, Harris in 1980 and Gordon Smith in 1991.

There is some evidence that some desultory bacteriology was done at Porton in the Great War for checking the safety of the camps water supply. This apart, microbiology at Porton is only half a century old. Nevertheless, and whatever Porton Establishment has been or is involved, Porton continues to be internationally acknowledged as one of the great place names of microbiology in the United Kingdom.

New Threats and Hazards 1980–1991

From 1976 until the late 1980s CDE was considerably involved in the Yellow Rain saga, which arose from claims of the use of chemical or biological warfare against the H'Mong tribes in Laos and in Kampuchea and specifically that certain mycotoxins (fungal toxins) known as trichothecene toxins were the agents involved.

The United States had, on the basis of early impressions, openly accused the USSR of a breach of the 1925 Geneva Protocol and of the Biological Weapons Convention of 1972, in supplying the agent of Yellow Rain for hostile purposes in Laos and Kampuchea. Many environmental samples from reported attacks were analysed at the Establishment. The symptomatology and clinical histories of victims were studied, as was the available information on the effects of trichothecenes on man arising in certain natural disease. Trichothecenes were also produced in small quantities from the Fusaria species of fungi and the various types extracted and identified for detailed study of their toxicology. Whilst analysis of samples at the Establishment proved negative, the epidemiological evidence led to the view that chemical attacks had occurred, albeit that the agent or agents remained unidentified. By the late 1980s Yellow Rain attacks were almost unheard of.

However, from 1980–1982 there was reported use of chemical weapons by the USSR in Afghanistan followed by undisputed reports of the use of mustard gas and nerve agents by Iraq

The safe disposal of old chemical munitions is one of CBDEs roles. This apparatus for opening artillery shells has recently been superseded by a remotely-controlled system. The chemical agent charging from such munitions is destroyed by burning.

The Range

In 1992 the range at Porton is a sanctuary for some 96 species of birds, almost 200 species of spiders, and innumerable varieties of fungi, orchids and lichens; the area has been designated a Site of Special Scientific Interest. A prime reason for the exceptional flora and fauna is that the chalk grass land is relatively undisturbed and untouched by pesticides, fertilisers and the plough. Whilst sheep graze parts of the range, in other areas the turf is grazed by a vast rabbit population. The short turf provides optimum conditions for the now rare stone curlew. Scrub, and notably Juniper bushes, is slowly invading the grassland where sheep grazed for centuries before the Army came to Porton. This scrub in turn provides a habitat for many nesting birds. Over 100 deer and badgers exist on the range. The wooded areas are carefully managed with conservation interests in mind. Studies on Porton's natural history have been pursued for some years by an active Establishment Conservation Group, which also hosts visits from other interested and involved groups and bodies.

Autumn at Old Lodge.
One of the drives near the plantations in the Old Lodge area of the Porton Range.

and Conservation

But the range is not only a vast 7000 acre nature reserve: it is an important archaeological area where so far more than 200 sites have been recorded. Some have been excavated but most remain untouched. There are 115 round barrows of the Bronze Age including the largest bell barrow in Wiltshire and 32 km of earthworks. Man has lived at Porton since early prehistory and his relics survive in barrows, cemeteries, earthworks, flint mines and enclosures. The flint mines at two separate sites of over 100 shafts each are important examples of Neolithic industry. The archaeological sites have been protected for decades, unlike the situation elsewhere, where the loss of sites to agriculture, to industry and land development, has been disastrous. In fact, most of the range has never been cultivated and can readily be described as a prehistoric landscape.

The state of the Porton range in 1992 emphasises the care taken to preserve defence lands. It also suggests that the environmental effect of disseminating chemical agents on the range in the considerable quantities that occurred notably between 1916 and the late 1950s has had little or no deleterious effect on the local flora and fauna. The ownership of the range by the Ministry of Defence has been a major factor in ensuring the preservation of a considerable heritage of natural history and archaeology.

In July 1992 English Nature and CBDE signed a Management Plan for the Site of Special Scientific Interest which constitutes about half of the 7,000 acres of Ranges at Porton.

The May 1988 visit by USSR military scientists and diplomats.

against Iran from 1983 and against the Kurdish element in Iraq, notably the infamous Halabja attack in 1988 and subsequent intensive use in offensive operations against Iran. The 1979 Sverdlovsk incident had aroused concern about the USSR's compliance with the Biological Weapons Convention. This, Yellow Rain and Afghanistan all combined to engender unease about the apparently broadening global threat.

In 1983, when Dr Watson left to become Director of the Building Research Establishment Dr Alan Bebbington, formerly Deputy Director (Chemistry) at CDE, was appointed Acting Director. After a short spell in the USA at the start of his career, Dr Bebbington came to the then Chemistry Research Section at Porton in 1953 and became Superintendent of the Chemistry Division in 1972. In June 1984 Dr Graham S Pearson, latterly Director General (Research and Development) in the Royal Ordnance Factories, was appointed Director of CDE.

The 1980s were marked by the re-appraisal of the biological threat, the assessment that recombinant-DNA techniques and

USSR officers visiting Porton during the Second World War. Seated with the Russians are Air Commodore Combe the Chief Superintendent and Brigadier R M A Welchman. In the back row are (left to right) O G Sutton, Lieutenant Colonel A E Kent, Edgar Bateman, Captain D C Evans and an unidentified officer.

At Shikhany; June 1988.
British scientists from Porton with representatives from other Ministry of Defence departments and the Foreign and Commonwealth Office made an historic visit to the USSR chemical warfare facility at Shikhany. Earlier in May, USSR representatives came to Porton. The only previous official USSR visit had been during the Second World War when the Red Army Officers visited Porton.

biotechnology might be misused to obtain an almost quantum leap in biological warfare potential by any nation which possessed or intended to possess such capabilities. Chemical and biological weapons were no longer fairly well separated methods of war; their agents now formed a continuous spectrum. Hand-in-hand with these newer hazards was the spectre of proliferation.

The USSR stated unequivocally for the first time in 1987 that it possessed chemical weapons and provided details to the international community during the negotiations for a Chemical Weapons Convention. In 1988, as part of confidence-building moves connected with the proposed Convention, a party from the USSR chemical warfare facility at Shikhany and other departments visited CDE for a week of visits and discussions. At the end of June in the same year there was a reciprocal visit to Shikhany by a team which included CDE staff. On both occasions the United Kingdom teams were jointly led by the Director of CDE and the United Kingdom Ambassador to the Conference on Disarmament in Geneva. Greater openness on these matters between the USSR and the West and the increasingly detailed negotiations for a verifiable and effective Chemical Weapons Convention were balanced by reported Libyan production of chemical agents at Rabta and intimations of even more proliferation occurring in many parts of the world.

However, whatever the hazards in future military conflicts, the United Kindom forces are probably still the best equipped in the world for chemical and biological defence. The newest S10 respirator, the No 1 NBC suit Mark IV and the array of sophisticated detection and monitoring equipment available in-service are unsurpassed. Training in chemical defence by the Army was considerably enhanced by the creation in 1979 of the

Field trials with helicopter-mounted chemical agent detectors in the 1980s on the Porton Range.

Porton Battle Run on the ranges. This unique facility enables visiting units to deploy realistically for 36–48 hours over many miles of the range with differing topography. The unit is exposed to realistic attack with agent simulants from the ground or air and can enact drills and adopt the full protective ensemble and practice decontamination. Their performance can be readily assessed. The Battle Run is managed and staffed by the Establishment and is utilised for training by United Kingdom army units. The chemical and biological defence readiness of the British Forces was exemplified in the Gulf following the Iraqi invasion of Kuwait in August 1990. Fortunately, the Iraqi chemical and biological capabilities were not used against the coalition forces; there can be no doubt that the high level of United Kingdom defence preparedness must have been a major factor influencing the Iraqi decision. Whilst the use of chemical agents against well protected forces was not likely to have been effective, as it had been against the relatively poorly protected Iranians or the unprotected Kurds, the hazards likely to be encountered by United Kingdom Forces were considerable. Further, our Forces had not been exposed to any such hazard since 1918.

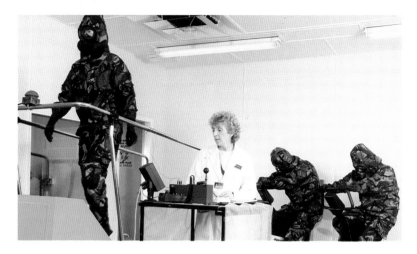

Evaluating the physiological burden of personal protection.

The protection of the body from chemical and biological warfare agents has to be developed with care. All effective protective clothing and respiratory protection can reduce fighting efficiency to a degree and the aim is to achieve maximum protection with a minimum physiological burden to the wearer. Hence the classical methods of human physiology, such as the treadmill seen here, are used to measure effects on breathing rates, body temperature and the circulation.

Operation GRANBY : The Gulf Hostilities and Operational Support: 1990–1991

The Iraqi invasion of Kuwait and its subsequent failure to withdraw by the 15 January 1991 deadline imposed by the United Nations Security Council Resolution 678, projected the Establishment into active operational support of United Kingdom forces in the Gulf. The Establishment devoted considerable resources which involved two-thirds of the senior staff for part of the time: this equated to the full time effort of a third of the staff; much other activity was necessarily curtailed. Contributions were made to the intelligence communities assessment of the threat, notably on characteristics of agents, the implications for British operations, the consequences of Iraqi deployment of ballistic missiles with chemical or biological warheads and likely scenarios for their use. The hazard distances which could arise from Allied conventional weapon attacks on Iraqi chemical and biological facilities were assessed; as were those which could arise from PATRIOT interception of SCUD-type missiles with chemical or biological warheads. Estimates were provided on the persistency of agents in the climatic conditions which existed in the Gulf. A considerable effort was devoted to an analysis of the likely effects of Iraqi chemical and biological attacks on Allied Forces at several fixed sites and in mobile operation states. Urgent and successful measures were taken to augment the already in-service chemical agent detectors and monitoring devices and an interim system for the detection of biological agent aerosols was designed, developed and dispatched to the Gulf, together with Service operators trained at the Establishment. For confirmation of such attacks and highly

The urgent needs for effective defences in the Gulf led to the rapid development of additional equipment and the instruction of servicemen in its deployment.

Here monitoring the environment by continual air sampling and subsequent analysis is being practised on the Porton Range.

The British troops in the Gulf war were the most well equipped for defence against chemical and biological agents. Clanging mess tins together was a useful means of local alarm.

specific identification of the agents, a system for collection of samples was devised, trialled, produced and deployed, together with trained Service personnel within three months.

Advice was constantly sought by and given to the Ministry of Defence, other Government departments, defence contractors, industry and individuals on the implications of chemical and

In the Gulf war this tented medical treatment facility makes use of the Porton liner concept of ensuring the gas-proofing of RAMC field hospitals and casualty clearing centres.

biological attacks by Iraq in Gulf conditions. Much advice was provided to the Service on decontamination topics and the agent persistency that might be expected in the climate and conditions of the Gulf. Most Western nations data on such matters had, of course, arisen from work which related to the more temperate conditions of a war in Europe. In extremely hot conditions certain chemical agents may present quite different and often greatly enhanced hazards. The potency of mustard gas may be increased almost two-fold with more rapid and complete vaporisation and the increased susceptibility of sweaty skin to penetration.

On medical countermeasures, studies were done and advice provided on control of infection in wounds and the management of wounds contaminated with chemical agent. The lesions produced in the skin by mustard gas are notoriously slow to heal; the Establishment devised a surgical technique to enhance the healing rate. A system for casualty monitoring was implemented in conjunction with the Department of Health, the National Health Service and the Armed Forces Medical Services, to provide advice on the medical management of any chemical and biological casualties in the Gulf and at British military and civilian hospitals.

The ability of the Establishment to respond so successfully to wide-ranging problems was dependent on the existence of multi-disciplinary teams of civilian and military personnel, backed by efficient trials, engineering and administration staff; a reflection of the tradition laid down at Porton after the Great War of 1914–1918 and continued thereafter. The magnitude of the activity at Porton is shown by the intention to record it in numerous individual Establishment reports during 1991. These will also identify topics that may require further consideration and work. Acknowledgement of the Establishment's role in the Gulf War was both widespread and at the highest level. The ability to act, as well as advise, within a short time scale was particularly appreciated. In recognition of their exceptional contributions to the Establishment's support of Operation GRANBY, Dr R J Powell was awarded the CBE, Dr G J Cooper, Mr J W Tindle and Lieutenant Colonel H D H Keatinge were awarded the OBE and Corporal M G Lee-Bennet, the BEM. A further eleven members of staff received letters of commendation from the Under Secretary of State for Defence Procurement.

After the ceasefire, the Establishment has continued to support activity relating to the United Nations Special Commission set up to oversee the destruction of Iraqi nuclear, chemical and biological weapons and of ballistic missiles. Professor Bryan Barrass OBE, as the then Superintendent of the Chemistry and

Decontamination Division was appointed as the sole United Kingdom member of the Special Commission set up by the United Nations Security Council resolution 687. Subsequently Professor Barrass and several other Establishment staff visited facilities in Iraq in the course of the Commission's work.

A British soldier in the Gulf drinks from his water bottle through a special tube built into his respirator. This was another 'first' from Porton.

The Future: Perceptions of Continuing Requirements

6

It may seem presumptuous to contemplate the unknown years ahead. In an ideal world effective and verifiable measures of arms control would have obviated the need for much of the role of the Establishment decades ago, but we do not live in an ideal world; nor are we likely to. Since the 1930s, some nations which have ratified international prohibitions on chemical and biological warfare have with certainty used chemical agents and may well have used biological agents. In other nations, whilst there may not have been use, there is good evidence of the capability to use. Some other nations have still to ratify the relevant arms control agreements and a few nations remain who have never signed or ratified. In addition to the existing 1925 Geneva Protocol and the 1972 Biological Weapons Convention, a Chemical Weapons Convention has just completed negotiation after 20 or more years. When this Convention is signed and ratified, it is likely to be several years before all its states parties can meet all its requirements. Destruction of chemical agent and weapon stocks and of production facilities is a costly and time consuming process. Even then, the verification of compliance with the Chemical Weapons Convention is a matter of such complexity as to be likely to necessitate the continued existence of CBDE as the focus of necessary research and advice. Similarly, it is likely that in the future some verification provisions will be applied to the 1972 Biological Weapons Convention. Microbiological research and biotechnological activity capable of misuse is ubiquitous. Microorganisms and toxins capable of use as biological agents exist in nature, evoke naturally occurring disease (unlike most chemical agents which do not occur in nature and have no alternative civil use) and are the subject of a great deal of study. Given this plethora of activity, the discrimination between innocent and civil activity, permitted biological defence research and prohibited misuse presents problems.

Against the background of such verification difficulties, there can be little doubt about the case for maintaining effective chemical and biological defence as an adjunct to arms control, in order to provide a deterrent to any aggressor contemplating the chemical or biological warfare option. CBDE has a major role to play in promoting the effectiveness of verification and, alongside arms control, maximising the effectiveness of export controls in this field. The early 1990s have seen great emphasis on control of dual-use exports which could be misused for chemical and biological warfare purposes. Effective controls which do not prohibit transfers of such materials for peaceful purposes need sound technical advice for enforcement. CBDE is already playing its part in the fields of chemical and biological export controls. Inevitably, all these developments provide a sound rationale for sustaining CBDE well into the future.

CBDE today
Comparison with the aerial views and plans of earlier years shows that many huts and minor buildings have been removed, as have most of the married officers' quarters. The 'Closed Area' has changed its outline to include a new car park and the Establishment has been considerably enhanced by now mature trees and shrubs.

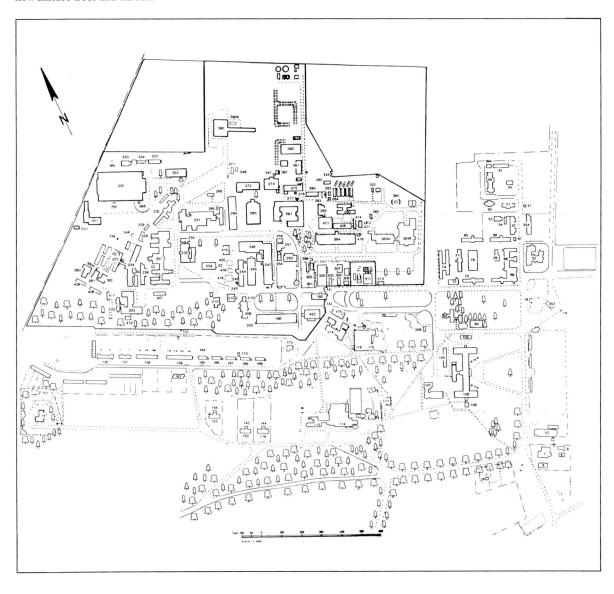

The late Dr J F S Stone, a distinguished archaeologist and a sometime member of the staff of both major Establishments at Porton, wrote an appendix for Kent's 'History of Porton'. In this he expounded the thesis that Porton had been the site of evaluations of experimental procedures some thousands of years earlier. The prehistoric flint mines, stock farming and fortifications could all be seen as man's earlier exploratory study in industry, agriculture and defence. Stone continued his theme with the local gun-flint industry of the Napoleonic era and concludes 'What more appropriate site could have been found in modern times to carry on such a tradition of experimental studies than in this central part of Wessex born of an old stubborn determination to resist and prevail? Yet no one could imagine for a moment that such a historical background in any way influenced the minds of the authorities charged with the choice and acquisition of this stretch of land as an experimental ground in the 1914–1918 war to meet and combat the German threat of Chemical Warfare'. It is difficult now to envisage the CBDE at Porton Down could discontinue the traditions of the last 75 years perceived by Stone, however fancifully, as stretching back into prehistory.

Because of the considerable military utility of chemical and biological warfare, the vulnerability of the military and civilian population of the United Kingdom to clandestine attacks and the particularly unpleasant hazards that would arise, it is certain that CBDE will continue to be seen as an essential part of the national defence programme, whatever levels of arms control appear in the future. No doubt the Establishment will suffer uncertainties and vicissitudes as it has in the past but we can be reasonably confident that in 2016 the centenary of CBDE will find the Establishment still active at Porton and continuing the traditions of service to the military customer which were first established in 1916.

At present, major international changes are afoot, particularly in the former USSR and Eastern Europe. There are uncertainties about the future role and nature of the United Kingdom's Armed Forces. These reflect a changing but not diminishing threat. World wide manifestations of proliferating capabilities for chemical and biological warfare reinforce the Latin motto 'Cave' which has been carried on the Establishment crest since at least the 1930s. We must indeed continue to 'beware' and respond to the technically challenging capabilities against which protection is required.

What is Chemical and Biological Warfare

Chemical Warfare

A chemical warfare agent has to be deployed so that it is inhaled as a gas, vapour or aerosol (a suspension of microscopic particles in the air) or as liquid droplets intended to contaminate the eyes and skin (some gases and vapours may also exert effects on eyes and skin). Agents therefore exert effects on the body after entering by either the respiratory portal, the eyes or the skin. Agents which can exert profound effects through more than one of these portals will be particularly hazardous eg the nerve agents or mustard gas.

Not all agents are lethal. Some, like the lachrymators (tear gases), are intended to harrass and be a temporary impediment. Others, like mustard gas are vesicants (blistering agents) whose effect may be profound enough to immobilise and hospitalise men for many weeks. Others, like the nerve agents, are intended to kill and can do so very quickly at minute doses.

Some chemical agents do not exist as a gas or vapour eg certain arsenical compounds. They are deployed as powders, as aerosols or as particulate smoke. Others exist as a liquid which gradually vaporises to a gas; here both the liquid and the gas will be toxic. A few agents can be released as gases from cylinders eg chlorine and phosgene. Most early chemical warfare was based on such use but this was soon superseded by the use of chemical munitions and other types of chemical weapons to deliver the agent directly on the target.

The purpose of chemical weapons is to maximise the dissemination of the agent on the target. The older cylinder method of dissemination relied on the wind to carry the gas to the target. Accuracy was limited by wind speed, wind direction, turbulence and the effect of terrain eg woods and valleys could cause diversions or delays. The danger of affecting areas outside the target, including friendly forces, was considerable. Shell, mortar bombs and aircraft bombs filled ('charged' was the traditional vernacular expression) with chemical agent could now be delivered on to the target by gun, mortar or aircraft with some precision. Wind direction was still important to obtain diffusion of agent within the target from the immediate impact area but chemical attacks were no longer critically dependent on the wind. The bursting of the munition on or over the target releases liquid droplets, aerosols or vapour (according to the nature of the agent and munition design). Chemical warfare is traditionally a tactical weapon for the battlefield but it can be used more strategically, especially by large-scale use of aircraft bombs or missile warheads, for attacks on rear areas, bridge heads, ports, airfields, the defence industries and, ultimately, civil populations.

Chemical Defence

The main aim of chemical defence is to protect the respiratory tract, the eyes and the skin. This can be readily achieved but troops would suffer some profound physiological and psychological penalties if they were to wear respirator, the NBC suit, NBC gloves and NBC boots continually, especially in hot weather. Such penalties would quickly affect fighting efficiency. The alternative is to know when a chemical agent hazard exists, so that the respirator and gloves can be put on. In the combat zone or highly vulnerable rear areas, troops will already be in their NBC suits, with respirators and gloves at the ready.

The approach of a hazard can be detected by automatic sensing of the air for aerosols or vapours, by battlefield intelligence, papers or paints which show by colour changes that agent droplets have descended from aircraft-borne sprays or air-burst weapons, by characteristic smells and other means. The ideal detector should run continuously and be remotely sited to alarm before the chemical agent reaches the unit, ship or facility that it is guarding and it should react in near real-time. Some detectors can also identify or discriminate between agents.

The protection given by the respirator depends on sealing off the eyes, nose and mouth areas from the outside air and allowing only agent-free air to enter the facepiece. This agent-free state is achieved by drawing the air through a canister containing absorbent charcoal to remove gases and fine filtration material to remove aerosols, smokes and other particulate agents. The NBC suit can also have absorbent charcoal incorporated in its air-permeable fabric or, it may be impermeable. Both concepts have advantages; the current British suit is permeable, the incorporated charcoal effectively prevents ingress of agent for a considerable period.

Prophylaxis against certain chemical agents can be provided by conveniently tabletted drugs to be taken in immediate anticipation of a chemical attack and immediate self-aid injection devices provide nerve agent antidote for unprotected personnel who have been unexpectedly attacked. Medical treatment can be highly specific or merely supportive. Often particular aspects of chemical agent poisoning can be treated by the armoury of drugs used in general medicine to relieve specific and life-threatening effects, such as lung oedema.

Collective protection can be built into fighting vehicles, ships, command posts, aircraft shelters and field hospitals or indeed almost any structure. Here air is processed in much the same way as for the individual respirator but on a larger scale. Capital ships may also have pre-wetting systems designed to prevent residual contamination hazards from nuclear, chemical and biological attack by continuously wetting the upper works and decks to minimise adhesion. Residual hazards may subsequently be detected by hand-held monitors and extensive chemical and physical decontamination measures are available to neutralise and remove any intractable chemical agent contamination.

Biological Warfare

Biological agents are usually living microorganisms eg bacteria, rickettsiae or viruses which cause infectious diseases. The term biological warfare is often taken to include the toxins; as does the 1972 Convention. Toxins, though not living, have their natural origin in certain species of micro-organisms, plants or animals ie their natural origin is biological.

Agents are either liquid suspensions of live agents or solutions of toxins, or their powdered forms. Biological munitions and weapons create aerosols of the agent which enter the body on inhalation to evoke infectious disease, or for toxins a toxic effect. Not all such infectious diseases or toxic effects need be lethal; in the same way that few naturally occurring infectious diseases are lethal. Some may produce a temporary period of debilitation which will put exposed personnel out of action for a few weeks eg influenza, tularemia. Some toxins eg Staphylococcus Enterotoxin B may evoke a quick and transient debilitation lasting less than 24 hours. Other live agents or toxins may produce a largely lethal effect eg plague, anthrax, botulinum poisoning.

Biological weapons or munitions will be designed to maximise the dissemination of agent aerosol particle in the appropriate microscopic size range when the device functions. Munitions are likely to be aircraft cluster bombs or missile warheads, rather than artillery rounds. Other weapons are likely to be sprays mounted in aircraft, drones, vehicles or ships or portable static devices capable of being emplaced and deployed in highly clandestine ways.

Biological warfare is very flexible; no other method of war is capable of use on the same strategic, tactical and small scales to produce, by the appropriate selection of agents, effects which can be lethal or merely incapacitating, protracted or short-lived and fairly rapidly or often with an incubation period of many days. A biological capability is likely to be much cheaper to develop than that for chemical warfare and the hazards and defence problems it evokes are likely to be more profound and complex.

Biological Defence

Much biological defence is subsumed in chemical defence ie the respirator will prevent inhalation of any aerosolised agents and protect the eyes, and although the intact skin is relatively resistant to biological agents, the NBC protective suit provides added protection. The critical aspect of biological defence is to know when to put on the respirator or have recourse to collective protection. Awareness of a biological attack must depend on battlefield intelligence, aerosol detection systems, other inferential means and adopting a protective state when high risk situations arise.

Prophylaxis by immunisation is possible for most biological agents and provides a first line of defence, as against naturally-occurring infectious disease. Antibiotics and anti-viral drugs can provide further protection and therapy. Because of the vast number of putative agents, rapid identification of the agent is important for the selection of appropriate therapy. Most medical countermeasures against biological warfare reflect those used against naturally occurring infectious diseases. Not withstanding, most civilised nations may have had little recent experience of many such diseases, which may now be endemic only in remote areas.

Arms Control

The use of chemical and biological agents in war is prohibited by the 1925 Geneva Protocol. Most nations have ratified this agreement, either in the 1930s or after the Second World War, but largely with reservations that have effectively made this a no-first-use agreement. States parties have, however, breached the agreement on occasions in the past eg Iraq by use against Iran and alleged breaches are numerous. The Protocol does not prohibit the possession of offensive capabilities, merely their use in war. Many original States Parties to the Convention entered reservations permitting realiation in kind and continued during the 1930s to maintain or acquire capabilities. The ability to retaliate-in-kind against non-signatories or even States Parties who saw advantages in breaching the Convention, was seen as a fundamental need by most nations for many years.

The inadequacies of the 1925 Geneva Protocol in respect of biological warfare were ostensibly remedied by the 1972 Biological Weapons Convention which was intended to ban the acquisition of a biological warfare capability and to supplement the ban on use in the Protocol. However, the Convention did not prohibit possession of production facilities and has, at the time of writing, no provision for verification of compliance. As an interim measure certain confidence building provisions were agreed at the Second Review Conference in 1986 and finalised by a meeting of national experts in 1987. Substantial improvements to the confidence-building measures regime were agreed at the Third Review Conference of the Convention in September 1991 at Geneva. States Parties are now required to make annual declarations of biological defence activities and other relevant information, as well as a once-and-for-all declaration of past offensive and defensive programmes. The Geneva meeting also agreed a mandate for an international group of experts to examine the feasibility of verification provisions: the experts first met in Geneva in April 1992 and again in November 1992, when CBDE representatives played a prominent role.

A Chemical Weapons Convention has recently completed negotiation under the aegis of the United Nations for over 20 years and will open for signature in January 1993. This Convention should have an intrusive verification regime and should, for chemical weapons, effectively underpin the prohibitions on use set out in the 1925 Protocol. The aim of the Convention is to provide a comprehensive, effectively verifiable and global ban on chemical weapons.

A Selected Bibliography

The number of sources containing information on chemical and biological warfare and defence is vast. Many such sources have information relevant to Porton Down but they are too numerous to cite here. Also, some information may be speculative or inaccurate. This bibliography is limited to sources in the public domain that provide substantial information about Porton Down and its activities; it is not a bibliography of sources on chemical and biological warfare and defence.

The Royal Engineers Experimental Station, Porton
Lt Col A W Crossley RE (1919)
Public Record Office: WO 142/265

Second report of the Secretary of the Chemical Warfare Committee (1922)
Public Record Office: WO 33/1014

Fourth and fifth annual reports of the Chemical Warfare Committee (1924 and 1925)
Public Record Office: WO 33/1049 and WO 33/1078

Sixth, seventh, eight, ninth and tenth annual reports of the Chemical Warfare Research Department (1926–1930)
Public Record Office: WO 33/1128, WO 33/1153, WO 33/1174, WO 33/1204 and WO 33/1231

Eleventh, twelfth, thirteenth, fourteenth, fifteenth, sixteenth, seventeenth and eighteenth annual reports of the Chemical Defence Research Department (1931–1938)
Public Record Office: WO 33/1272, WO 33/1298, WO 33/1330, WO 33/1359, WO 33/1389, WO 33/1443, WO 33/1484 and WO 33/1565

(This series of annual reports includes the headquarters branch for chemical warfare and defence within the Directorate of Artillery, the Master General of the Ordnance and the War Office, its experimental station at Porton, the process research establishment at Sutton Oak, extramural studies in universities and industry, and the Chemical Warfare (later Defence) Committee. These reports provide the most complete official account of events and attitudes from 1922–1938).

'The Microbiological Research Department, Ministry of Supply, Porton, Wiltshire'
D W W Henderson
Proc Roy Soc B (1955) **143** pp 192–202

A History of Porton
Lt Col A E Kent DSO MC RE (1960)
Public Record Office: WO 188/802
(This includes a preface written in 1992 which gives biographical details of the author)

A brief history of the Chemical Defence Establishment, Porton (1961)
Public Record Office: WO 188/785
(Written by C G Trotman, though authorship is not apparent in this booklet)

'The Microbiological Research Establishment, Porton'
C E Gordon Smith
Chemy Ind (1967) **9** 338–346

'Porton's Story told'
G B Carter
Scope (May 1975) (a now defunct MOD Procurement Executive house journal)

Eight papers by CDE authors on several aspects of the Establishment's work in a special issue
Chemistry in Britain (1988) **24** No 7

'Microbiological war and peace'
C E Gordon Smith
PHLS Microbiology Digest (1990) **7** (2) 48–51

'The Chemical Defence Establishment'
The ASA Newsletter 90–3 Issue No 18 (June 1990)
(In a series of articles entitled 'National Laboratories'; no author is shown)

'Gruinard Island returns to civil use'
Graham S Pearson
The ASA Newsletter 90–5 Issue No 20 (October 1990)

'A Tale of Porton Down'
Gradon Carter
Focus (1991) April pp 10–11 (The house journal of the Ministry of Defence)

'The Chemical and Biological Defence Establishment, Porton Down, 1916–1991'
G B Carter
RUSI Journal (1991) **136** No 3 pp 66–74

'75 years of chemistry at Porton Down'
G B Carter
Chemistry in Britain (1991) **27** pp 1095–1096

'75th Anniversary; the Chemical and Biological Defence Establishment (CBDE) Porton Down: 1916–1991'
Gradon B Carter
The ASA Newsletter 91–4 Issue No 25 (August 1991)

'The Microbiological Research Establishment and its precursors at Porton Down: 1940–1979. Part 1. Biology Department Porton 1940–1945'
G B Carter
The ASA Newsletter 91–6 Issue No 27 (December 1991)

'Part 2. The Microbiological Research Department and Establishment 1946–1979'
G B Carter
The ASA Newsletter 92–1 Issue No 28 (February 1992)

'Biological warfare and biological defence in the United Kingdom 1940–1979'
G B Carter
RUSI Journal (In press)

Index

Acknowledgements

Many people have provided information for this book; it would be impossible to list them all. Several people have scrutinised the drafts and I am grateful to them; particularly David Arnold-Forster. I am also grateful to Julie Venner for typing and to the staff of HMSO.

A Note About the Author:
G B Carter ISO CBiol MIBiol

Gradon Carter joined the Microbiological Research Department at Porton in 1948, working in experimental pathology, virology and the administration of research until 1976, when he went to the Ministry of Defence in London. He returned to Porton in 1979 and headed the Technical Intelligence and Information Section at what is now the Chemical and Biological Defence Establishment, until 1990. Since then he has pursued various studies, often on historical aspects of chemical and biological warfare and defence, on arms control and on foreign activity. He is the author or co-author of many papers in scientific journals, dealing with the rapid laboratory identification of viruses such as those of smallpox and vervet monkey disease; and the pathology of experimental air-borne infection. Recent papers reflect his later interests and include several written to mark the 75th Anniversary of the Chemical and Biological Defence Establishment.

'Printed in the UK for HMSO
Dd 0295554, 12/92, C30, 565533, 36145